D0287959

WILDERNESS
OF MIRRORS

THE LIFE OF
GERALD BULL

WILDERNESS OF MIRRORS

THE LIFE OF
GERALD BULL

DALE GRANT

Prentice-Hall Canada, Inc., Scarborough Ontario

Canadian Cataloguing in Publication Data

Grant, Dale
   Wilderness of mirrors: the life of Gerald Bull

ISBN: 0-13-959438-8

1. Bull, Gerald, 1928-1989. 2. Firearms industry
and trade - Canada. 3. Munitions - Canada.
4. Murder - Belgium - Brussels. 5. Firearms
designers - Canada - Biography. 6. Space Research
Corporation - Biography. I. Title

HD9743.C22B85 1991   338.4'76234'092   C91-093172-0

© 1991 by Dale Grant

ALL RIGHTS RESERVED. No part of this book may be reproduced in
any form or by any means without permission in writing from the
publisher and the author.

Prentice-Hall Inc., *Englewood Cliffs, New Jersey*
Prentice-Hall International, Inc., *London*
Prentice-Hall of Australia, Pty., *Sydney*
Prentice-Hall of India Pvt. Ltd., *New Delhi*
Prentice-Hall of Japan, Inc., *Tokyo*
Prentice-Hall of Southeast Asia (Pte.) Ltd., *Singapore*
Editora Prentice-Hall do Brasil Ltda., *Rio de Janeiro*
Prentice-Hall Hispanoamericana, S.A., *Mexico*

Editor: William Booth
Cover Design: Tonia Craan
Illustrations: Tony Horvath
Interior Design and Composition: Olena Serbyn
Manufacturing Buyer: Lisa Kreuch

ISBN: 0-13-959438-8

Printed and bound in the U.S.A. by R.R. Donnelley & Sons Company

1 2 3 4 5 RRD 95 94 93 92 91

To the boys and the girls at the
Living Hell Cafe

ACKNOWLEDGEMENTS

It goes without saying that a book on a subject as wide and as varied as the life of Gerry Bull is a creation of many others besides the person who wrote it. It is also inevitable that any attempt to list the contributions of the several hundred people who in some way aided in the production of this work, will be deficient. Even to simply mention those who provided professional skills or insights is a chancy business. To those I missed, my profound apologies and grateful thanks.

First, to my friend, Jo Hershoff, my appreciation for her reading and checking of my drafts, and for correcting my lamentable errors in grammar. To Mike O'Brien, my editor at *The Wednesday Report*, a special thanks for his support and sound advice, and to John Reed, the *Report*'s London editor, a deep appreciation of his comments and assistance. At *The Toronto Star*, the aid of Gerry Hall, Paul Watson and Jack Granek is gratefully acknowledged, as is the help of David Todd of Southam News, Sam Hemmingway from *The Burlington Free Press*, and Claudio Gotti of Europea. From the field of television news, Jim Reed and Lawrence Morton of CTV's W5, Anne-Marie Dussault and Jean-Claude Lesloch of CBC's *Le Point*, Jane

Corbin, from the BBC's *Panorama*, and Kelly Creighton and Trish O'Brien of the CBC's *the fifth estate*, a special vote of thanks. To those who helped with inspiration, research and explanations of technical points, I remember Martin Shadwick, Brian MacDonald, Cathy Murphy, Charlie Murphy, Fred Prong, Bob Willard, Jim Gotleib, Sannu Molder, Dyllon Roach, Bob Rodden, George MacDonald, Rene Halle, and David Stroud.

To Michael Bull and his mother, Mimi, a greater debt is owed. In spite of being told beforehand that they would not like some of my conclusions, they gave generously of their time and made me appreciate the fierce loyalty of the Bull clan. There are also many who gave counsel, insight and advice, who, for various reasons, cannot or did not wish to be named. For trusting me with their confidences, another round of applause. For the few, the very few, who lied and sent me on false trails, to hell with you.

Toronto
February, 1991

CHAPTER 1

And the night shall be filled with music,
And the cares that infest the day,
Shall fold their tents like Arabs,
And as silently slip away.

> —*The Day Is Done*
> by Henry Wadsworth Longfellow,
> Gerald Bull's favourite poem

There is a picture buried in the files of a hundred media organizations and, no doubt, those of a score of foreign intelligence services, as well. It shows the hallway of a luxury apartment building at 28 avenue François Folie, in the Uccle district of Brussels, Belgium. Outside the door of a sixth floor *piede à terre*, a vase of flowers stands beside a dark, dried stain, on a carpet that was already red. For someone, or some group, it is a final proof that their mission was accomplished.

According to the Brussels police, "A person or persons not currently known to the authorities," walked down that hallway early in the evening of March 22, 1990, and fired five shots from a silenced pistol, into a Canadian businessman who was about to open his apartment door. The body of Dr. Gerald V. Bull was still warm when the horrified woman, who was to have joined him for dinner that night found him, scant minutes later. The killer, or killers, left behind a corpse with $US20,000 in its pockets, and a still-unresolved murder case, which sparked a series of sensational revelations by the global media about a cannon so gigantic it could shoot around the world.

For once, truth exceeded the fantasies of pulp spy thrillers. Tales of "Super Guns" were followed by exposés of secret arms transfers to Third World nations, and missile-warhead designs for Iraq. The stories led to numerous examinations of the career of a true Canadian prodigy. Even a hardened newsman like NBC's Tom Brokaw would shake his head and mutter, "There's a movie here, for sure."

National hero and space researcher, weapons designer, convict and bankrupt, he was also a multi-millionaire arms dealer and a technical prophet. Dr. Gerald Bull was, in parts, Tom Swift, James Bond and an industrial magnate, rolled into one. That one searches in vain for another person to compare him with, illustrates his uniqueness. (Some have suggested the legendary Howard Hughes, but there is no comparison. Hughes was an eccentric insider. For all his accomplishments, Bull was always on the fringes of power.)

Yet, in spite of all the coverage, the shape and meaning of his story remains tantalizingly out of reach. It somehow resists the normal process of investigation. The frustration of the many journalists who have covered the story is revealed by one scribe's despairing comment. "The damned thing is like jello."

In the fields of anecdote and information on the life of Gerry Bull, questions become like dragons' teeth. They produce more and more of their kind and, in the end, there are no more answers to beat them down with.

So, paradoxically, what would normally be the harder thing for a writer to do—to portray the character, outlook and psychology of a man who spent much of his existence in secrecy and obscurity—becomes the easier task. For here, the question is not who murdered him, but why he became the man he was.

Scarcely a week after his assassination, a story broke in the English media, about a series of gigantic tubes being produced in the steel-mill town of Sheffield. The disclosure that a British company had been involved in a deal that could have given the militarily ambitious Iraqi leader, Saddam Hussein, access to a so-called Super Gun, with which he could bombard his neighbors' cities, caught the British public unawares.

The news broke on Thursday, April 12, 1990, after a customs search of a ship, which had been loading cargo for Iraq at the North Sea port of Middlesborough. The inspecting officers seized a number of pipe-like sections, one meter in internal diameter, and fabricated from

high-grade steel. Their destination had been the "Republic of Iraq Ministry for Industries and Petrochemical Project, Baghdad, Iraq," but the customs men, and the officials from the U.K. Ministry of Defence's Royal Armaments Research and Development Establishment, whose advice they sought, were in no doubt that they had an altogether more sinister purpose. The "pipes," they said, were, in fact, sections of a huge gun barrel.

The British public had been given what journalists like to call a "story that will run and run." Within days, there were seizures of other parts of the Super Gun, as it had become known, in Greece and Turkey. The story had all the right ingredients; a recognizable bad guy in the Iraqi president, and a maverick scientist, and it quickly acquired human interest, in the form of an innocent truck driver, locked in a Greek jail while his load of gun components was investigated.

It would be several months before the Iraqi invasion of Kuwait gave the public the opportunity to understand precisely what lay behind the seizures. Some were quick to link it with a similar incident at London's Heathrow Airport only two weeks earlier, when a consignment of alleged triggers for a nuclear device was intercepted, in an elaborate sting operation, by the U.K. and American authorities. Later, the same public would come to recognise the name of Gerry Bull, but at first, only a handful of insiders, who had been following the twisted trail that linked the eight years of war between Iraq and its unpopular neighbor, Iran, with a number of shadowy contracts secured by European firms, readily made the connection between the seizure of the "pipes" and the shooting in the Brussels apartment building.

One person who did make the connection was U.K.-based defense journalist, John Reed. Two years earlier, at an international machine-tool exhibition, his interest had been aroused by an admission from representatives of the West German company, Gildmeister, that their firm had major contracts in connection with what was evidently a high-tech defense project, being masterminded by an associated company, Gildemeister Projects. Reed did not obtain all the answers that he was seeking, but learned enough from the carefully phrased answers to realize that the country involved was Middle Eastern and, most probably, either Egypt or Iraq. Later, he was able to eliminate Egypt as the customer. What worried him was something more than the fact that the phrases being used were familiar as cover-ups for work on nuclear weapons. The more questions he asked, the more he realised that, although the U.K. government was adamant that it did not encourage trade in defense material with Iraq, the U.K. and most other European countries had become—either directly or indirectly—deeply involved in a shadowy trade with the Baghdad authorities.

Survival has been at the heart of Iraq's search for arms. As the Gulf War against Iran raged, Iraq needed the latest weaponry, if it were to survive. The companies that it chose as its suppliers needed full order-books, if they were to be among the survivors in a tough trade. The middlemen, through whom both sides dealt, are renowned for their survival instincts.

When the war first erupted, the Baghdad government was able to seek out sources of supply, in the knowledge that there was no shortage of Westerners who wanted to see its Iranian enemy toppled. It was then that the authorities in several countries turned a blind eye to Iraq's attempts to short-circuit their regulations governing the export of war supplies.

One such country was Italy, where, a few months before the seizure of the "pipes," the business community was rocked, but by no means surprised, by a series of allegations concerning exports of mines and other munitions by the leading defense contractors. Another was Belgium, which has a history of *laissez-faire* in its control of arms dealers extending back into the 1950s. Regional development agencies, drumming up support for local industry, have hosted visits by parties of Third World military officers and, according to one former Bruges businessman, there is no official discouragement of the activities of "export and import" businesses that solicit local participation in arms deals.

It was in Belgium that Dr. Gerald Bull found, in munitions manufacturer PRB, an early partner in his business ventures. It is no coincidence that PRB has often been linked with ammunition exports, not only to Middle Eastern countries, but also to South Africa.

In the Gulf War, however, European companies like PRB faced fresh competition for orders. Brazilian manufacturers delivered artillery rocket launchers and armored personnel carriers to Iraq, at prices well below those quoted by the longer-established suppliers. As the war progressed, probably some two hundred deadly G-5 long-range howitzers, along with thousands of tons of artillery shells and propellant, produced in South African factories, swelled the convoys of trucks on the newly constructed super-highway linking Iraq with the Jordanian port of Aqaba. There, ships could discharge their cargoes, free from the risks of mining and Iranian air attack.

It was against this cut-throat background that British businessmen booked their seats on what some came to call "The Baghdad Shuttle,"' in a sales effort that appeared to be in total contradiction to what their government said was happening.

While the arms pipeline had ensured Iraq's survival, it had been a close thing. Like Israel and South Africa before it, Iraq's thoughts turned to self-sufficiency. It had a rapidly expanding manufacturing sector, but it lacked the crucial technologies that the West would be less than willing to surrender.

The essence of technology transfer to a developing nation is that you don't give your customer access to technologies that might turn him into a competitor. If Iraq was to fulfil its military ambitions, it had to give its technical intelligence services a full shopping list. It would, for example, have needed CNC, computer-directed machine tools, and access to supplies of the latest generations of advanced composite materials, propellants and lightweight metals. When South Africa had acquired the G-5 howitzer, it had done so within a partly-developed manufacturing infrastructure, and had been able to draw on its own world-class experience in some areas of metallurgy and detonics—the science of explosions. Iraq had already established itself as an emerging industrial force, but it had to move its technology onto a fast track, if it was to do all that its leaders demanded.

When it came to acquiring closely held technology, Iraq had two advantages. It knew that even the high-tech companies needed orders, but more importantly, it had access to an extensive network of Iraqi businessmen based in Europe.

The British public first became aware of the activities of this network in 1989, when their business newspapers carried stories of how Iraqi interests had acquired control of machine-tool maker Matrix Churchill, and were bidding to take over the Belfast, Northern Ireland, factory that had formerly belonged to the failed aircraft manufacturer, Learfan. Some reports suggested that the stricken business was to be equipped to undertake isostatic pressing, a key technology in advanced-weapons production. Certainly, it was expert in carbon-carbon composites, materials of particular interest to designers of aerospace structures, and also used for the protection of missile warheads against the fantastic temperatures they encounter on re-entering the earth's atmosphere. In 1989, though, nobody read too much into the fact that the company formed to take over the Learfan works, SRC Composites, provided a direct link between the Iraqi network and Gerry Bull.

The connection between Matrix Churchill and SRC Composites lay in a company known as the Technical Development Group (TDG). At one stage, they had a common director, Dr Fadel Jawad Kadhum, an Iraqi lawyer who eventually resigned from the TDG board, in January 1990, when unease was beginning to mount over the connection. TDG was owned by Al Arabi Trading, a company with a Baghdad address and two directors who were understood to be officials in their country's state-owned engineering business. Dr Kadhum was also a director of a company known as Canira Technical Corportaton, in which the shareholders were TDG and Dr Bull's Geneva-based SRC Engineering.

Suggestions that Matrix Churchill—a highly respected name in the machine-tool industry—was supplying machine tools to Iraq's arms industry had a familiar ring for journalist John Reed. "There was something that did not add up," he recalls. "Less than a year earlier, the company's public relations consultant was telling me that Matrix had aspirations in the defense industry. It was very much like what

Gildemeister had told me. He certainly did not tell me that it was controlled by Iraqi interests. Yet, as soon as there was a suggestion that it might have been supplying tools for defense plants, he was on the telephone telling me that there was nothing to worry myself about. I had known this man for some years...he's a good PR man, but I can tell when he is running scared. My guess was that his clients were very worried about the possible consequences of disclosure of a link with Iraqi arms programs."

By late 1989, there were signs of increasing concern, in at least the U.K., about the extent to which the tentacles of the Iraqi procurement machine had reached into European industry. Another U.K.-based company, Meed International, which had an Iraqi director, had been working closely with Ali Abdul Mutalib Ali, the commercial attaché in the Iraqi embassy in Bonn, West Germany, and a representative of Nassr State Enterprise, to organise a competition to supply machine tools to Iraqi industry. Nassr is the organization that has played an important role in establishing state-owned ammunition factories in Iraq. Meed was also reported as having approached Astra, an ambitious U.K. ammunition manufacturer, with proposals to involve it in a scheme that would have by-passed U.S. restrictions on the export of sensitive technology, and given Iraq a turnkey munitions plant.

There was to be no contract in this instance, but Astra was already set on the course that led to its 1989 acquisition of shell-maker PRB from its Belgian parent. Its then-chief executive, Christopher Gumbley, was to be the man who joined Gerry Bull for lunch on the fateful day he was shot down.

The Iraqi agents targeted the sources for the technology they sought with precision. Astra's plans to increase its ammunition sales had been thwarted by an agreement between the British government and its principal competitor. By the time Meed International came knocking on the door, it desperately needed orders to survive.

Meanwhile, Sheffield Forgemasters, the firm that was to make the "pipes" seized at the Middlesborough docks, definitely had the equipment to produce a gun barrel of the kind that might be required for a Super Gun. In 1987, a company representative had told John Reed that it could overcome the technical problems involved in producing a barrel with a core capable of withstanding the erosive effects of what it described as "advanced propellants." Certainly, it was not without experience in producing gun barrels using novel technology. It had, in fact, been a supplier to BMARC of Grantham, England, a subsidiary company of the Swiss Oerlikon group, which was later to be taken over by Chris Gumbley's Astra Holdings Limited.

Yet, Sheffield Forgemasters was not alone in exploring ways to counter erosive effects in gun barrels. The offer document that Astra Holdings issued, before buying PRB in August of 1989, details "anti-erosion liners" as one of the activities undertaken at the Belgian company's three-hundred-hectare plant at Balen, close to the Dutch border. However, the Sheffield company may be among the world leaders in mating such a liner with a conventional steel casing, and has openly discussed its gun-making techniques at major international arms exhibitions.

A common thread that runs through the companies with an Iraqi connection is their need for major contracts. Outwardly, Sheffield Forgemasters had recovered well from the financial problems that beset it in the mid-1980s, but it had recently embarked on a major capital-investment program, and its chief executive had been among the most vocal critics of the high level of U.K. natural-gas fuel prices, which did not endear him to the Thatcher government. The company was basically in good shape, but was still facing tough times.

Sheffield Forgemasters' customer had been a subsidiary of Bull's SRC group of companies, which had assured its management that the "pipes" were indeed for a petrochemical project. Even so, the steelmen were not entirely satisfied, and say that they referred their fear that they could be supplying components for a chemical-weapons plant to the U.K. government's Department of Trade and Industry. It was only after they had been reassured by the bureaucrats that the order seemed legitimate that they got to work on producing the Iraqi order.

As the Middlesborough customs officers were studying the seized "pipes," their colleagues farther south had swooped on a second company. Walter Somers Ltd. was typical of the old established businesses in the heartland of the country's engineering industry. Well respected, and with a reputation for quality engineering, it nevertheless faced an uncertain future as a member of the troubled Eagle Trust group, following the disappearance of the group's chief executive, John Ferriday, in the wake of allegations against him in a £13.5 million fraud scandal.

It, too, needed more orders, and it certainly wasn't the simple forge and "metal-bashing" shop that the company would soon attempt to portray itself as. Somers, which has provided propeller shafting for warships of the Royal Navy, and has admitted to having the capability to produce tank-gun barrels and breech mechanisms, has also undertaken design and manufacture of isostatic presses. Yet, here again, Walter Somers executives had suspicions that the order from SRC might have been for something other than a petrochemical plant. Its managing director voiced his concerns to his local Member of Parliament, Sir Hal Miller, who, in turn, told three government departments about the Iraqi order. Whether these included the intelligence services remains unclear but, eventually, the company felt that it was able to proceed without fear of contravening the regulations. Eventually, the customs officers who descended in force on the Somers works came to the conclusion that the order had, in fact, been for parts of the aiming and elevation mechanisms for the Super Gun.

The British customs men had only exposed the tip of an iceberg. As the weeks passed, there were further seizures, throughout Europe, of heavy steel parts, produced in response to orders for Iraqi "petrochemical projects." In place or in transit, components were found in Italy, Turkey, Greece, Spain, Switzerland and Germany. A mysterious Athens-based company called Advanced Technology International (ATI) was found to be coordinating the effort. Gerry Bull's SRC companies were soon identified as the suppliers, and the investigations into his activities continue to this day.

For the story of Gerry Bull and what he accomplished is not over. To understand where it is going, and from whence it came, one must go back beyond the beginning of this century.

CHAPTER 2

A newspaper obituary covered Gerald Bull's formative years with the brief words, "Born in 1928 into a large Catholic family in North Bay, Ontario, Bull was a child of the depression. When his mother died in 1931, his father sent him to live with a relative, who later placed him in a in a Jesuit college." While this précis of the first sixteen years of Bull's life is right on points, it hides a larger story of a closely knit family shattered by economic and personal tragedy.

Gerald Bull's son, Michel (frequently called Michael), president and manager of his father's Space Research Corporation International, would later say, "My father never talked about his younger years...it's only now, after his death, that we're beginning to discover some of our relatives."

He sees a "certain saving grace" in the fact that his father's spectacular demise is helping reunite members of a clan now scattered across Canada, with only the vaguest knowledge of each other's existence. For Gerald Bull is survived by seven long-lost brothers and sisters, whose fragmentary knowledge of his younger days adds up to a comprehensive picture of what has been described as a "void of conflicting information." They have shed light on the early development of Gerald Bull's character that go a long way toward explaining his future actions.

The family's roots go back over two hundred years in Canadian history, to when the Bulls first settled in the Kingston, Ontario, region at the beginning of the nineteenth century, as wealthy immigrants from the English Midlands. Industrious and strongly Anglican, they quickly prospered in business, farming and law, and their descendants intermarried with the Scottish and English United Empire Loyalists who had preceded them to the area, after fleeing the American Revolution in the late 1700s. Yet, from the beginning of their stay in the New World, there has also been a French strain in the Bull genealogy. Among Gerald Bull's antecedents was a Madeleine de Montford, a refugee French countess who came to North America after the demise of the Bourbon kings in the French Revolution. The very name of his father—George Lewis Touissant Bull—illustrates the continuing Gallic connection.

George spent his life as a lawyer, a profession his son would later denounce as "charlatans," and "a bunch of sleazes, who I learned you can't ever trust." According to his older sister, Vivian Harrison, now a widow living in Mississauga, Ontario, the comment speaks volumes about Gerald Bull's feelings toward a father he felt had showered him with love and then abandoned him. "I think his memories of our father were very confused, even at a young age...love and hate is a fair description."

In the modern world, where family traits and characteristics have less and less impact on young people's lives, the old cliché, *like father, like son*, has almost faded away. Yet, in the case of Gerald Bull, the similarities with the life and career of his father are quite remarkable. Rises to prominence and collapses into bankruptcy, depression and alcohol would be the courses of both men's lives. Each, in turn, would recover and face the world with vastly changed attitudes.

George Bull was born in Trenton, Ontario, on July 14, 1877, the son of a wealthy landowner named Henry Bull, and Charlotte, née Gothard, Bull. Like his son-to-be, he was a brilliant student who advanced beyond his years. In 1897, at the age of twenty, he graduated at the top of his class from Toronto's Osgoode Hall Law School, but had to wait a year to be admitted to the bar, as twenty-one was then the minimum age for practicing law.

What he did after that is lost beyond recall of his surviving kin, but researcher Fred Prong, of the North Bay Genealogical Society, has found three faded letters in the Copy Book of the lawyer's library in the North Bay courthouse, which show a George L. T. Bull was practicing criminal law in the remote town of Burks Falls, Ontario, as early as 1903. In the archives of Osgoode Hall, there is a stained, grey card that states he later practiced in North Bay as early as 1909, though the North Bay telephone directories list him as a lawyer in 1907, and give his home address as Trout Lake, then a rural area on the city's outskirts.

In 1909, George Bull took a step that was to cause much of his family, back in Trenton, to disown him for over two decades. In an era when religions routinely preached that adherents of other faiths were doomed to hellfire and damnation, he ceased to be an Anglican. The Catholic diocese of Sudbury has a parish record of his baptism into their church on February 20, 1909, at the age of thirty-two.

Three days later, the same records show that he married nineteen-year-old Gertrude Isabelle LaBrosse, in St. Mary's of the Lake church. Born June 27, 1890, she was the daughter of Napoleon and Florence (née Barker) LaBrosse. Her father was a prospector who had achieved millionaire status in the 1850s, by discovering a good share of the mineral wealth that is still a foundation of the Sudbury-North Bay economy today.For the up-and-coming young lawyer, it was a match that met the social and economic criteria of the day, and the difference in age was not unusual at the time. It was also a great and enduring love.

"My mother and father adored one another," Vivian remembers. "I cannot recall them ever having an argument, or even a harsh word...in many ways they were like one person, they were always holding hands when they were together."

The couple's first child, Bernice Gwendolyn Florence, was born nine months later, on November 22, 1909. That year, the phone book showed Bull's home listing on Copeland Avenue. According to Bob Willard, of the North Bay Historical Society, "Copeland was then the poshest street in the city...big houses, with lots of room for children and servants."

As was common with Catholic families of the time, Bernice's birth was followed by a steady stream of brothers and sisters. Henry Bull arrived in 1911, Philis in 1913, and Charles Esmond in 1916.

An archivist, familiar with the time and region, said, "In those days, women kept giving birth until they either reached menopause or bled to death in childbirth...It's unusual that all her children survived past the age of two...its a definite sign the family was well off, compared to the average, and very lucky to boot."

North Bay phone directories show George Bull moved four times, after the birth of Bernice on Copeland. The family residences were on streets that were respectable, but progressively less wealthy. This is indicated by the 1917 directory listings, which show George Bull's new home address as 2 Kehoe Street. Willard describes the neighbourhood in that period as "not wealthy compared to Copeland, lower middle class is more accurate."

It was George Bull's last change of residence in the city, and would be the family home for thirteen years. There the Bull's fifth child, Clyde Morgan, would be born in 1918, followed by daughter Vivian in 1921.

By the early 1920s, George Bull was taking an active interest in provincial politics, as a member of the Conservative party. While the Osgoode Hall card claims he was elected a member of the provincial legislature for the riding of Sturgeon Falls "in the Conservative government of Howard Ferguson," (1923-1930) the information is incorrect. The archives of the Province of Ontario show that, while he did run in the general election of 1923, he received only 605 votes, and was obliterated by the Liberal candidate.

George Bull's clientele and reputation expanded during the Roaring Twenties, as he began to specialize in defending companies accused of criminal acts. Increasingly, his work involved travel throughout Ontario, and he represented many clients before the provincial Surpreme Court in the capital of Toronto.

At home, George Bull was a stern, but loving, patriarch who ran his household with an iron hand. Vivian recalls that her brother Henry had excelled in hockey as a teenager, and had been approached by National Hockey League teams to become a professional. George Bull forbade it, as too dangerous and an unfit career for someone of their social standing. According to Vivian, Henry, who died in 1974, after running a men's-wear store in Brantford, Ontario, for most of his life, "regretted the decision to the end of his days...he had been a marvel on skates."

Some family sources have used terms like "prominent" and "lucrative" to describe George Bull's legal career, and claimed he was a "brilliant and innovative defender of his clients." This may have been true, but the city directory shows he never occupied any of the prestigious law offices close to the North Bay courthouse. His office listings show a series of what Fred Prong describes as being "modest chambers on secondary streets." While a frugal George Bull might have avoided the more prestigious and more expensive addresses of the city's legal lights, Prong says it shows his career was more likely "solid but not overly dramatic."

The seventh child, Ronald Bull, was born in March of 1923. Now retired, he lives in Toronto, and spent most of his career in the private-investigations field, including a period as a security officer for Toronto's York University. As a boy, he knew both the comfort of an upper-middle-class life and the cold reality of survival living. "I think we were the first generation of Bulls that *had* to work for a living." he says.

In January of 1925, Gertrude Bull gave birth to yet another son, Frank. Like his brother Ron, he would serve in the Canadian armed forces during World War II, in British Columbia and Alaska. After a somewhat controversial career as a stock promoter in Vancouver, he now lives in Chilliwack, British Columbia.

He also remembers his early days in a loving family, with a father he describes as "sensitive, well-educated and compassionate." He recalls his father coming home in tears after losing a murder case, in which he believed the accused man was innocent. "They hung you in those days," Frank points out, "and they did it damn quick, too."

Without pay, Frank's father did additional legal work and lobbied to have the sentence commuted, but was not successful. "My dad took it hard," Frank says. "If he believed in a client, he fought for them as if they were one of his own family."

On March 9, 1928, when Gertrude bore him his next-to-last child, Gerald Victor, the fifty-one-year-old George Bull must have felt a certain degree of satisfaction with his life. On June 16 of that year, the provincial government of Conservative Howard Ferguson appointed him a King's Counsel, then a prestigious legal mark of professional ability and political connections. His personal wealth had also been increased by the recent inheritance of several family properties in the Trenton area, and, like many of his social class, he had begun to invest heavily in the stock market, especially mining issues. Times were good, and the local economy was booming. George Bull was respected in his community. He had a good house and gilt-edged investments that he believed would take care of him in his old age, and provide a sound future for his children.

In October 1929, the crash of the stock market in far-off New York City heralded the start of the Great Depression. Like millions of other people, George Bull saw the hopes and stability of his existence rudely shattered.

It is difficult today to comprehend the totality of that world-wide economic collapse, and its quick impact on resource-based local economies like that of North Bay. For, if the major cities of North America suffered, rural Northern Ontario was scourged. Hunger stalked the lives of at least half the population. In the nearby town of Sturgeon Falls, every resident, including the mayor, was on a government dole of six dollars a month. Food donations by the nearby Dokis Indian tribe, in the form of fish and game, are still gratefully remembered by older residents.

In North Bay, over eighty percent of the businesses collapsed, and the practice of law was no exception. Worse, George Bull's share of his family wealth had suddenly become a house of cards. Rich as he might have been, on paper and in land, he had followed common practice and bought most of his stocks "on margin," meaning the initial investment was as low as five percent of value. This was fine in a decade of rising prices, but when prices fell to pennies on the dollar, the buyer was stuck with the original debt. Within a year, George Bull's loans were called by the banks, and he was forced to sell the house on Kehoe Street, under threat of seizure, and mortgage his other properties to the hilt, in a desperate attempt to stay afloat. After twenty-four years, the name of George Bull disappeared from the North Bay listings forever.

In 1953, relatives painted a picture of him moving to Toronto "in 1931," and quickly establishing another "thriving law practice," but both Ron and Frank agree that was not so. Even the vaunted KC after his name, and the connections he had in Toronto, were of little help in a city that was itself reeling from economic collapse, and had a sudden surplus of legal talent.

The Bull family moved into a rented house on Glenholme Avenue, in what was then the north of the city. George took a small office in the downtown business area, and once more hung out his shingle.

"I don't think he had many clients at the time...few people had any money left by then," is how Frank Bull puts it. To economize, Vivian recalls that they didn't even have a phone at home.

Already weighed down by financial problems, George Bull was to be hit with a worse disaster the following year. In March of 1931, Gertrude gave birth to her last child, Gordon, and fell ill with complications. Infection set in and, five weeks later, on April 1, she died in Toronto's St. Joseph's Hospital, at the age of forty-one.

"We were a close-knit family...haughty and proud of who we were, even in adversity," Ron Bull says, "but the death of our mother changed everything."

Vivian Bull put it more succinctly. "I don't think our father ever really recovered from the death of our mother."

George Bull suffered a nervous breakdown, and began to drink heavily. While, outwardly, his attitude toward his children remained unchanged, he became increasingly moody and withdrawn from the world around him. Devastated, the fifty-four-year-old widower gave up his Toronto law practice and returned to the old family homestead in Trenton, with the nine children who still remained at home. Bernice, by this time, had married a William Costello and moved to the hamlet of Sharbot lake in Oso County, north of Kingston.

For three years, George Bull lived in virtual seclusion, while his spinster sister Laura, a retired nurse, became a second mother to the young Gerald and his brothers and sisters. Vivian Bull recalls her as a kind but stern woman, who quickly gained the children's affections. She also remembers Gerald as "an extremely active child," whose antics in church once got her a clip on the ear from Aunt Laura, for being distracted by her younger brother crawling under the pews.

While still grieving from the loss of his wife, George Bull recovered from the worst effects of his despair within a year of Gertrude's death. He stopped drinking heavily, and tried to re-establish a local law practice, to meet his mounting debts and support his family. But, as Frank Bull remembers, "He found some work, but it wasn't enough."

Later, in 1933, while George Bull's debts continued to mount, Laura fell victim to cancer, and died in the summer of 1934. The care of the children then passed into the hands of a hired housekeeper and their twenty-one-year-old sister, Philis.

The year 1935 saw the family struck by two more events, which led to the little clan's final disintegration. In July, the banks foreclosed on the homestead that had been Bull land for five generations, and George Bull fell in love again, at the age of fifty-eight.

Vivian Bull describes Rose Bleeker as "a spoiled, beautiful woman, who none of the family liked...she didn't understand children at all."

A distant relative of Gertrude's, and in her early fifties when she met George Bull, she was a widow twice over, who had dissipated most of her inheritances in attempting to follow a career in classical music.

With a new wife who had no intention of playing mother, and with less than a month before he would be evicted, George Bull gave up the struggle to hold his family together. George and his new wife moved back to Toronto, where they took a rented apartment, and George again established a law practice, in partnership with an old friend named Ike Weldon. It was to be a pale shadow of his former career, and never amounted to more than a subsistence living. Whether out of guilt or a simple lack of interest, he had little further contact with his children. When he finally retired to Trenton, in 1943, he and Rose spent their lives in isolation until his death in 1949, at the age of seventy-two.

Before leaving Trenton, George Bull simply turned his older sons and daughters loose in the world, and distributed the other children to various relatives. Four-year-old Gordon was sent to Winnipeg, Manitoba, to live with an uncle from the LaBrosse side of the family. He served in the Canadian army during the Korean War, and then became a policeman in Markham, Ontario, for most of his life, before leaving for higher-paid work in industrial security. He now lives in Winnipeg with his own family.

Henry Bull, then twenty-four, left to take a laboring job back in North Bay, while the nineteen-year-old Charles stayed in Trenton to finish high school. He would work in a factory during World War II, and later become an engineer with Canadian Westinghouse.

Clyde Morgan also stayed in Trenton, but was forced to leave school and take a job in forestry. During the war, he volunteered for the army and served in the European campaign. Afterward, he joined Ontario Hydro, and moved to Niagara Falls, where he married, and lived until his death in 1980.

Of the two sisters still at home, Philis stayed in the Trenton area and, shortly after, married John Hayes. Now widowed and ill at age seventy-seven, she still lives near the old Bull homestead. Vivian Bull was sent to another uncle, who was a pharmacist in nearby Burford.

She would do war work and secretarial studies, before marrying in the late 1940s.

Lastly, Francis, Ronald and Gerry were sent to live with their sister, Bernice, in Sharbot lake. While she has been described as his "third mother," the relationship, by some accounts, was not a happy one. In a nation still gripped by the Depression, no one in the town of Sharbot Lake was living very well. According to one set of relatives, the hard-pressed young woman and her husband resented having the children dumped on them. She only took it on out of a sense of duty, since George Bull was unwilling, or unable, to contribute to their keep.

Brothers Frank and Ronald both say Bernice was not abusive, nor did she scrimp on looking after them for the next five years. Yet they were several years older than their little brother, and Vivian thinks Gerry may have badly missed the close affection he was used to.

In the Oso County archives, there is an attendance record for the 1936-37 school year, showing that Gerry, Ronald and Francis attended SS #2, a remote, one-room school outside Sharbot Lake. One of the students who attended the school was Donald Antoine. Now sixty-seven, he is a retired pharmacologist who has recently returned to the town where he grew up. He remembers Gerry Bull well, and even met with him several times in Toronto, in the late 1940s.

"You say he was unhappy here. I don't recall that at all. Times were tough then, but people up here had gardens and cattle, so there was always enough to eat." Antoine describes the Costello residence, which still stands at Zeeland Road and the present Highway 38 outside of Sharbot Lake, as "not much more than a shack...but that was common then."

He remembers that Bill Costello was the local cab driver and town bootlegger during the Prohibition era. "He would take his cab down south, and pick up the booze for the other bootleggers in the area, as well as his own stock. I think he got paid twenty-five cents a case for making a delivery. There wasn't any shame in it then, everybody in the town knew what he was doing. Hell, they were his customers." Antoine stressed that the Costellos were as poor as anyone else in the region. "He didn't get rich off of it...it was more of a survival thing."

The first summer after he attended SS #2 in Sharbot Lake, the nine-year-old Gerry had a sudden break in his fortunes, one that was to make possible his entire future career. Sent to spend the summer with another set of relatives, he spent his vacation on a sixty-eight-acre orchard, two miles east of Kingston. The property was owned by another member of Gertrude Bull's family, Philip LaBrosse, and his wife, Edith. She had won the Irish Sweepstates in 1931 and collected $130,000, the equivalent of several million dollars today.

In a 1953 *Maclean's* magazine article, entitled, "Jerry Bull, Boy Rocket Scientist," Edith LaBrosse described the kid who showed up at their door as an "insecure, shy and nervous little boy," who was desperately in need of love and affection.

Gerry was quoted as saying, "I have no recollection of my real mother, but no boy ever had finer parents than Aunt Edith and Uncle Phil."

Edith LaBrosse commented, "That year he had his first real Christmas...He had had few toys in his life before."

The story is that he liked the LaBrosses and the orchard so much that he wanted to stay, and made every possible excuse for remaining. As summer faded into fall, the LaBrosses drove him up to Sharbot Lake, only to discover on their arrival that Gerry had deliberately left all his clothing and books back in Kingston. He was carrying an empty suitcase.

There was nothing for the LaBrosses to do but take him back to Kingston. Childless themselves, they didn't seem to mind, but a problem soon arose. They had arranged to spend that winter in Florida, so what to do with Gerry Bull?

Ed Zarichny is currently the principal of Kingston's Roman Catholic high school, Regiopolis-Notre Dame. Known as Regiopolis College when Gerry Bull attended it, from 1938 to 1944, it was then an all-boys school, run by the Jesuit order, and most of its 150 students, Gerry Bull included, were boarders.

Zarichny has taken an interest in the early career of what he calls, "perhaps the school's most interesting graduate." After pointing out that the records from those days were not very comprehensive or well kept through several changes of administration, he still finds a puzzling lack of information about Gerry Bull.

The LaBrosses told this story of Gerry's admittance. When the headmaster, the Reverend Austin Bradley, was presented with the undersized, nine-year-old boy, he said, "Sorry, the laddie's too young."

Yet the LaBrosses say they got his agreement to keep Gerry at the school until they returned from their vacation. Two months later, when they came back, the headmaster's attitude had changed. "He's a fine boy that; an excellent student. Its very bad changing schools in mid-term. Gerry should stay here."

Zarichny finds that a little hard to swallow. "I am at a loss as to how he was placed. The school at that time had very high admission standards...I can find no other case like it."

The school records show Gerry Bull entered grade nine in 1938. At age ten, this put him four years ahead of the normal admission age.

It may be that the LaBrosses, being from a prominent and wealthy family, were extremely persuasive. Zarichny believes it is possible they made a substantial donation to one or another of the school's charitable funds, an action that would have aroused no approbation at the time.

That Bull's records only survive for grade nine, where his marks ranged from 90 in English to 56 in arithmetic, and grade thirteen, where his scores ran from 95 in geometry to 55 in physics (a strange showing in view of his later career!), is not unusual in an institution that has undergone several changes of management. What Zarichny finds odd is the lack of information on his file card. The spaces for relatives, next of kin, and who to contact in case of an emergency, are blank. All that shows is his name and an address, Glen Lawrence Orchard (Blvd.), RR #1, Kingston, Ontario.

In talking to classmates of Bull's, still residing in the area, Zarrichny gained the impression that "he was very much a loner, which is not surprising, considering he would have been socially underdeveloped compared to his classmates. In those days...his aunt's placement of him [in a boarding school] would have been more a way of having him looked after, rather than as a means of getting an education."

Yet one can assume kinder motives. The LaBrosses traveled widely, and for extended periods. That they took the responsibility for seeing to Gerry Bull's education and upbringing, shows a genuine concern. According to Vivian Bull, Edith LaBrosse, over a period of time, came to deeply love Gerry Bull, perhaps in compensation for the loss of her own two children within months of their births, and her inability to bear more. In fact, she describes Aunt Edith as becoming "terribly possessive...she later tried to keep him apart from the rest of the family."

The following school year, he lived with them at the Orchard, and only occasionally attended Regiopolis, since bitter winter storms often isolated the homestead. Gerry thrived in this new environment, and the fierce curiosity that was to mark his entire life first became evident. His aunt Edith recalled that, even then, "he was always building airplanes."

Starting with prefabricated balsa-wood kits, he made, flew, and wrecked them as fast as he could persuade his aunt and uncle to buy more. He then moved on to building models of his own design. The delicate adjustments of wing angles and balance, which made the difference between a model soaring or tumbling to the ground, fascinated him. Amidst his glue pots, paints and cutting table, the ten-year-old boy began keeping a careful record of the efficiency of his designs.

Gerry also began writing poetry, which, he said in 1953, was "pretty bad...I'm glad none of them survive." Most were about the orchard surrounding the LaBrosse house. To a boy who had been tossed from pillar to post, it represented an island of stability in his life. This otherwise-energetic child spent considerable time strolling from tree to tree, examining each in turn, until he could recall the individual health of hundreds of them. It was as if they were his best friends.

Perhaps they were. Child psychologists say that being ahead of your age group in a high school often results in being frozen out of the mutual-support groups that teenagers form. Such kids are sometimes considered "weird," and become targets for ridicule, pranks, and even assaults by older bullies.

That didn't happen to Gerry Bull. Invariably, his classmates speak well of him, and stress that his youth, "didn't seem to matter," even though he was small for his age. Although he took little part in the team sports that were a big part of the school's life, it wasn't held against him.

George Vosper, today a real estate developer in the Kingston area, shared Bull's interest in aircraft when they were both in the school's model-airplane club. "He seemed to be very quick to understand the designs," Vosper recalls. "Everyone knew Gerry was very bright."

Five other people say that, too. They also say they didn't know him very well, and no, they can't remember anyone who was his friend. Years of classes and sharing cramped rooms, and no one knew the name of his aunt, or his father, or even recalls him saying anything about his life. There are no personal anecdotes about Gerry Bull from his high-school days. In the end, no one there knew him at all.

In 1942, the LaBrosses decided to sell the orchard and move to Toronto, where they bought a house at 21 Belvedere Boulevard, in the affluent Royal York area. Gerry Bull went with them, and attended a local Catholic high school for one term. The next year, he returned to Regiopolis to complete his secondary education as a boarding student.

In the summer of 1944, after graduating at the age of sixteen, he went to work for the new owner of the orchard that held so many happy memories. In addition to his labors, Bull enroled in nearby Queen's University, for a partial year of freshman studies and membership in a wartime officer-training program.

But Queen's was only an interval. In Toronto, Philip LaBrosse was considering the future of his brilliant young ward.

CHAPTER 3

Today, the University of Toronto has some 3,500 faculty members, and 54,312 students. Even its highly specialized Downsview Institute of Aerospace Studies has nineteen professors, and over a hundred graduate students. The thousands of high-school graduates who seek admission to the University of Toronto each year must endure a months-long, bureaucratized selection process that one present student describes as "about as personal as getting your driver's licence."

The idea of a relative making an appointment with a professor, to discuss the admission of a student who had not yet filled in a single form, brings smiles to the faces of this generation of university administrators. That a professor would call Gerry Bull in for a ten-minute chat, and then say, "OK, you're accepted," causes laughter and comments like, "Sure were different days then, eh?"

In September of 1944, when Philip LaBrosse walked into the School of Practical Science on College Street, for his meeting with the professor in charge, the University of Toronto had 1,040 instructors and 7,158 students. While academic qualifications, in the sense of a student's ability to handle the rigorous curriculum, were not for sale, it was still an institution where money, connections, and social position played a crucial role in student selection. Apart from a few bursaries and scholarships, for "the deserving needy," few sons, and fewer daughters of the working class would even dream of such schooling.

This was to change dramatically with the end of World War II. The waves of returning servicemen had access to a system of government-funded educational support that allowed many, no matter what their background, to take advantage of higher education.

Unlike the First World War, when Canadian universities had virtually closed down, because educated young men flocked to the colors to become the junior officers of mass armies, enrollment actually increased in the second global conflict. This was a result of government policy. It was recognized that the new age of technological warfare needed men trained in arts and skills not previously required of soldiers. From 1939 on, graduating classes at the University of Toronto expanded, their members voluntarily enlisting in the services, virtually *en masse*, when their studies were complete.

The need of a war economy, for trained scientists and engineers, forced the government to divert many of them into civilian industrial activities. Even men who were already serving on the battlefields were recalled, to take up business and academic positions.

Thus, the Aeronautical and Civil Engineering programs of the university, in 1944, came under the direction of T. R. "Tommy" Loudon, a distinguished graduate from the class of 1905, who resigned his commission in the army to return to Toronto.

That same year, Philip LaBrosse wrote to Gerry Bull in Kingston, and asked if he would like to become a doctor, since he was "...sure your admission can be arranged." Gerry wrote back, and said no. But he had heard of the University of Toronto's brand-new, four-year course in aeronautical engineering, and he wanted that.

So LaBrosse went downtown to arrange it. At first, he was put off. "It's too difficult a course for a sixteen-year-old to start," Professor Loudon told him. LaBrosse asked him not to decide until he had a chance to talk to the young man himself.

Gerry came to Toronto, impressed the professor, and was declared admitted. Events would show that it was a brilliant, intuitive decision on Loudon's part. With his acceptance, Gerry moved into the Belvedere Boulevard house with the LaBrosses, and commuted each day by street car to his classes at the old, Gothic building on College Street.

His first four years at the university were a repeat of the Regiopolis story, with the exception that neither his marks nor the recollections of his contemporaries give any cause to call him brilliant. "He certainly didn't stand out," is how retired Doctor of Aerophysics, Ben Etkin, a professor of Bull's, recalled him.

Once again, people remembered him as pleasant and affable, but recalled no friends, and nothing of his life outside the school. "It wasn't until the 1950s that I heard Bull mention the LaBrosses, and their role in his life," said one classmate. "Even then, it was only a passing reference."

With marks that are described as "strictly average," Bull graduated in 1948, with a Bachelor of Applied Science in aeronautical engineering. He then took a drafting job with the A.V. Roe aircraft company, near Toronto.

The urgent needs of the war had accelerated aircraft development during the time Bull was studying. The time of the piston engine and the propeller, as state of the art, was over. The jet-turbine engine that propelled the deadly German Messerschmitt Me-262 fighter, in the last days of the conflict, was under rapid development in the U.S., Russia, Great Britain and Canada. But the great power available from this revolutionary power source had literally hit a brick wall—the sound barrier.

The days when men could incorporate intuition, and an "it looks right" approach, into the mathematics of aircraft design were over. Even for subsonic aircraft approaching the barrier, design now had to center on the problems presented by shock waves that seldom occurred in low-speed, propeller-driven aircraft. To produce practical, supersonic aircraft required a revolution in fuselage and wing design, which could only come from basic scientific understanding of the phenomena involved.

During Bull's undergraduate days, aircraft development had almost come to a stop, because these phenomena were not understood.

So new and unknown was the field that Bull's courses hardly mentioned the subject, but he was fascinated by the riddle of the shock wave. Unfortunately, there was no opportunity to work on supersonics at A.V. Roe, or anywhere else, for that matter. That changed late in 1948, when the University of Toronto established an Institute of Aerophysics for research and teaching in supersonic aerodynamics, under Dr. Gordon Patterson.

Patterson was one of the new type of scientists produced by the war years. Not only was he brilliant in his field, he was expert in the planning and management of scientific projects that involved hundreds of people and large sums of money. Better still, he understood the dynamics of the political world outside the laboratory, where funds and support had to be acquired.

A graduate of the University of Toronto in 1935, with a Ph.D. in physics, he went to Britain as scientific officer with the Royal Aircraft Establishment, until 1939. He then headed the Aerodynamics Department of the Australian Aeronautical Research Laboratory. From 1945 to 1947, he was a research fellow at both the California Institute of Technology and Princeton University. Returning to the University of Toronto in 1947, he was a perfect choice to head an institution that was to explore uncharted realms of science. He remained its chief until his retirement in 1974, a reign of almost three decades.

The Institute's initial funding, and much of its ongoing support costs, were made available by the Defence Research Board (DRB) of Canada and, while it did produce graduates with Masters and Doctorate degrees, it did not fit the standard picture of a school where learned teachers impart knowledge to receptive scholars.

Supersonics was then so unexplored a subject that the students had to work on individual research projects and teach themselves. Accepted students were handed research assignments by the DRB, and they received two thousand dollars a year, as an honorarium. This, in effect, made them employees of the DRB. The impact of this on Gerry Bull's life was to be greater than on any of his fellow students.

These men were selected with great care, since the program could only accommodate twelve students in total. The Ph.D. requirement called for a minimum of three years, and only four students could be accepted in any one year. Gerry Bull was one of the first. He quit A.V. Roe and applied for admission to the program. His competitors were all older men, many of them veterans with wives and children. Bull, at the age of twenty, and still looking younger than his years, at first appeared to the selection committee to be too immature to gamble with.

It was Patterson's recommendation that got Bull accepted. He recognized that Gerry had an all-too-rare quality that the institute urgently needed. "I had more brilliant students academically," he would later say, "but he had shown tremendous energy...a terrific ability to stick with a tough job and get things done, no matter what the obstacles."

The student that nobody knew, the loner child who sought solace in things as diverse as an orchard, poetry and the sleek lines of Spitfires and Folk-Wolf fighter models, was not a student anymore. All the drive and dedication that had been building up inside of him for fifteen years had found an outlet, at last. From this point on, there would be no lack of anecdotes and strong impressions about Gerry Bull. The frightened boy, from a world gone topsy-turvy, suddenly found himself a power, and he loved it. Pictures of him from those times inevitably show a grin. There is a sense of energy in the way he leans forward at his desk, a bounce in his step as he climbs a ladder over some experiment.

And why not? In an age where supersonic flight has been around longer than most people alive today, its difficult to appreciate the sense of challenge that men like Bull felt, as they pushed into the frontiers of high-speed flight. Their first task was to design and build the instruments for investigation of this new world and its often-baffling effects. The need was to take the airplane into the laboratory, and see how its shape behaved in hypersonic airflows under close, scientific scrutiny.

Along with fellow-student Doug Henshaw, Bull's first task at the institute was to create a small prototype for a hypersonic wind tunnel, the basic tool of high-speed aerodynamic research. Simple in concept, the device consists of a strong tank, with powerful pumps that remove the air to create a vacuum inside. A quick-release valve, or shutter, sits between the tank and the actual tunnel, where a suspended model can be observed in the airflow created by snapping open the shutter. While the airflow only lasts a few seconds, its speed can reach many times that of sound.

Dean Patterson soon found out what his words of praise for Gerry Bull could mean in practice. In the cramped working quarters of the Practical Sciences Building, Bull and Henshaw discovered that the components of their first, seven-foot-long tunnel wouldn't fit. Bull decided there was no time to rebuild it, so they would have to enlarge the space into Dean Patterson's next-door office. Patterson arrived the next morning, to find his desk crowded into the corner, and a large valve protruding through the wall.

"That was just the start," Patterson recalled later. "I was only beginning to get acquainted with Gerry Bull."

The model wind tunnels got progressively bigger, and the incursions into Patterson's office grew with them. Finally, Bull simply removed the whole wall, and Patterson came in one day to find his office had almost vanished. To get to his desk, he had to climb over the top of the wind tunnel. Worse, Bull and Henshaw would come in and stand on his paperwork, to reach various components of the system.

If being jolted out of his chair by the ear-splitting shriek of air rushing through the tunnel at three times the speed of sound, less than two yards from his seat, wasn't enough, he came in one day to find his work space filled with thousands of glass splinters. Bull's latest model had shattered the observation windows.

"I think he was getting fed up, and I don't blame him," Gerry Bull was later quoted as saying.

Fortunately for Patterson, the Canadian air force was persuaded to donate land for a new operations site in the Toronto suburb of Downsview, where the DRB provided funding for a new building with plenty of experimental and administrative space.

On September 26, 1950, with the Union Jack flying in the background, Patterson "was proud to announce" the official opening of the new facility and its full-scale, hypersonic wind tunnel, which was made possible by a $350,000 grant from the DRB. Among those attending the opening were the president of the university, Dr. Sidney Smith, Air Marshal W. A. Curtis, Chief of Staff of the Royal Canadian Air Force, and a host of dignitaries from the United States, Australia, New Zealand and South Africa. Prominently featured was Dr. Orland Solandt, chairman of the DRB.

Dr. Solandt gave a speech, in which he said, "When the Defence Research Board was formed in 1947, it was clearly recognized that research in the universities was the foundation on which rested all the applied research in the country...if the Board was to accept responsibility for all aspects of defense research, it must therefore give effective assistance in developing the strength of the universities."

Referring to the interests of the DRB in investing in universities, Dr. Solandt said another purpose was "...to ensure that the universities produced an adequate flow of well-trained research workers in fields of special interest to defense."

The opening ceremonies were widely and enthusiastically reported by radio and newspapers, where it was lauded as an example of the close cooperation between the university and the military. Today, the plaque commemorating the DRB contribution hangs out of sight, in a room at the Institute's library reserved for historical documents. The department is no longer proud of its military roots.

That the institute was almost totally supported by the armed forces and the DRB aroused no questions in an era when the Gouzenko spy scandal, the Berlin airlift and the Korean War made many average Canadians believe another world war was imminent. They, and the newspapers they read, supported military research. The thought that the atomic and hydrogen bombs might be heralding an end to centuries-old means of national and ideological struggle was not yet in evidence. Terms like MAD (Mutual Assured Destruction) would take another decade to evolve.

Typical of the war feeling was how the red scares and the McCarthyism of the United States spilled over into Canada. The idea that there were traitors among us, who needed to be rooted out, gained wide, if passive, acceptance. The spirit of the times can be captured in a parliamentary vignette from 1952. Conservative MP and future prime minister John Deifenbaker asked the Liberal minister of justice if he was aware of the statements made over Communist Chinese radio by a Dr. James Endicott of Toronto, in which he "speculated" that Canada was manufacturing biological-warfare weapons on a DRB site at Suffield, Alberta.

Besides dismissing the statement as untrue—which it was—the minister assured the house that such people were under "close surveillance by the Justice Department." His comments were greeted with applause from government and opposition benches alike.

As in the rest of the developed world, the traditional barriers between Canada's armed forces, industry and scientific institutions were rapidly dissolving, in the rush to advance military-related technologies. The roots of what American president Dwight Eisenhower would later characterize as "the military-industrial complex," and

Nikita Kruschev in the Soviet Union termed "the metal eaters," had formed as quickly in Canada as anywhere else.

Yet the case can be made that there was no other way to do it, especially in the aeronautical sciences. Scientists and engineers needed ever greater sums of money to pursue ever more complex research. Industry needed that knowledge to produce both civilian and military products. Soldiers, sailors and airmen wanted high-technology weaponry to stave off the mass armies of an Eastern Bloc that loudly proclaimed it was marching "toward the world victory of socialism."

With the Cold War now dead and buried, it may be impossible for most of us alive today to appreciate the view of a generation of scientists, many of whom had come of age in the fires of a global war. There was a common belief that their travail had been the result of weakness—weakness, not only on the political front from the likes of Neville Chamberlain, but in the field of technology, where the initial superiority of German and Japanese weaponry had wreaked havoc on allied forces.

The idea of deterrence, that strength and firmness could provide a shield against war itself, was very strong, and not much questioned, even by those of a liberal bent. Strange as the words may sound to a 1990s ear, the basic outlook was humanitarian, and sincere in its efforts to guarantee peace through strength.

That the view would curdle in the years ahead and become a sterile exercise, could not be foreseen. The isolation of the Canadian military, and that part of the scientific community that supported it, from the broad spectrum of contemporary Canadian society was still in the future. Thus it was with pride and broad social support that young scientists and engineers, such as Gerry Bull, turned their efforts to creations of an essentially warlike nature.

CHAPTER 4

The wind tunnel that Gerry Bull did so much to bring to completion still operates at the University of Toronto's Downsview facility. The silver-painted, forty-seven-foot-diameter sphere of its vacuum tank towers over the utilitarian brick building it stands beside. Several generations of students and professors have used it to advance human knowledge of aerodynamics. They are still using it.

While most major science projects today are preceded by years of studies, evaluations, and political and bureaucratic bickering, Patterson, Bull, and their colleagues put the tunnel and its mass of ancillary equipment together in less than eighteen months.

"There was nobody looking over our shoulders then," is how Bull described it in 1987. "Patterson would have thrown them out for trespassing on our ground."

Not only was Gerry working on the tunnel, but he had to complete his master's thesis on the subject, at the same time. Delivered on September 15th, 1949, it was a four-part study of the theory and practice of advanced wind tunnels. He would later say, of this time, that, "I think it was the most exhausting thing in my entire career." When Bull finally left the Institute of Aerophysics, he was fifteen pounds lighter than when he went in, and "on the edge of a nervous breakdown...we could not spare ourselves."

In 1947, the LaBrosses moved again, purchasing a brand-new house on Riverside Drive, only blocks away from their old residence. While Gerry continued to live with them, the LaBrosses did not see that much of the driven young scholar. His aunt said, "Gerry was working much too hard. On the nights he didn't stay at the Institute, he would come home, have dinner, and go to his room to study. At twelve, when we were going to bed, we would knock on his door and tell him to get some sleep. Through the crack underneath the door, we would see the light go out. He would wait until we had gone to bed, and then he'd get up and continue studying."

Bull later described the time. "If I got three hours sleep a night, I was lucky...I hardly knew if I was coming or going."

Some idea of the pressure he was under can be gained from the story behind the September 26, 1959, opening of the wind tunnel, an event presented by the Toronto *Telegram* as "a production of cool, deliberate scientific research."

Patterson, Bull, Glass and the other students were working night and day to finish on time. The afternoon before the grand unveiling, they were finally able to give the device a test. After the sphere was evacuated by the pumps, the shutter button was pressed. While the air screeched through the tunnel, no shock wave, the sign of a supersonic airflow, appeared in the viewing glass.

The scientists exchanged stunned glances. Could all their calculations, and the expenditure of what was, for the time, a huge amount of money, have been for naught?

The problem was actually simple. The packing that sealed the plates of the vacuum sphere was leaking. To replace the material required the removal and replacement of some four hundred large nuts and bolts. This took the frantic men until eleven at night. Since it took another two hours for the sphere to be evacuated for another test, Bull and two mechanics volunteered to wait, while the others went home and caught some sleep.

Try Number Two was no better. As a supersonic airflow was established, and the dazed men started to congratulate each other, a titanic bang ended their reverie, and the whole building shook. Inside the tunnel, two long pieces of shaped wood, which gave the tunnel its airflow configuration, had been ripped loose from their bolts and hurled into the sphere. While the new problem was also solvable, repairing the damage meant taking off all the nuts and bolts again. With the official opening less than twelve hours away, Bull and the mechanics wearily went back to work with their wrenches.

Fortunately for them, Dean Kenneth Tupper, head of the university's engineering department, happened to driving by the Institute and, seeing the lights were on, came in to see what was happening. Volunteering his services, according to one story, the dean threw a smock over his suit and crawled into the sphere, to help loosen the bolts from the inside.

Others had said that *drafted* was a better word than *volunteered*, and that the surprised dean was greeted by Bull with a tossed wrench and the cry, "You've got to help us."

Whichever way, Bull's statement that, "We'd never have been able to finish it if the dean hadn't worked like a galley slave beside us," rings true.

When the work was finished, at 3:30 a.m., no one had the energy to test the machine again. After the dean treated the workers to breakfast at an all-night diner, Bull went home for a couple of hours sleep.

Returning to the institute at ten o'clock that morning, Bull started up the pumps for a final test. This time it worked perfectly. The question was, would it do so again?

That afternoon, with the dignitaries assembled on the reviewing platform, Air Marshal Curtis pushed the button to give the tunnel its official start. Nothing happened—and down in the front row of watchers, Gerry Bull started visibly trembling. Beside the air marshal, Patterson reached around him and gave the button a harder push. The circuit closed, and the tunnel started up with a piercing whine—Bull had come through.

His reward, if such it was, was more work and a better understanding of who really employed him.

Canadian military research, especially operational research in anti-submarine warfare (ASW), had progressed well during the Second World War, and it made valuable contributions to the allied effort. Yet it was essentially a series of expedients, which had short-term objectives with no form or overall pattern.

With the return of peace, and before the start of the Cold War, much of this work ceased, and many of the bases involved were reduced to caretaker status.

Driven by the vision of "our gallant Russian allies," as the wartime press had called them, turning into the Red Menace, the establishment of the Defence Research Board (DRB) of Canada in 1947 was a remarkably farsighted act, on the part of the Liberal government of Louis St. Laurent and the leaders of the Canadian armed forces. Directly under the Ministry of National Defence, it provided an integrated framework for military research, and was implicitly aimed at supporting an independent Canadian defense industry and the indigenous development of high-tech weapons for national defense.

Part of the DRB's structure was a web of advisory committees, composed of Canada's senior scientists and university heads. In close contact with the highest levels of the military, they gave strategic advice on program development. Coordination was also established with the more civilian-oriented National Research Council of Canada (NRC).

Better, from the point of view of fundamental, theoretical research, its funding of university programs allowed it to provide a flow of basic information to the operational stations it now controlled. For, whether army, navy or air force, all the various research and test establishments that had grown up on an *ad hoc* basis in the war years were combined in one organization, which could provide direction, allocation of resources, and inter-service cooperation, in fields as varied as electronics, Arctic clothing and aircraft development. Installations as far afield as the Defence Research Establishment at Fort Churchill, on Hudson Bay in northern Manitoba, and the experimental station at Suffield, Alberta, which handled defensive/offensive research in chemical and biological weapons, and the Naval Research Establishments in the Maritimes, were brought under a single roof.

Also included was an army station known as CARDE—the Canadian Armaments and Research Development Establishment at Valcartier, Québec. Formed in 1943, it had pursued an independent existence, before the formation of the DRB, as the army's major artillery proofing and evaluation range.

Under army control, its first superintendent had been Dr. D.C. Rose, the Scientific Adviser to the Chief of the Canadian General Staff. He remained in charge during the difficult transition period to DRB control but, in October of 1947, he was replaced by Dr. W.B. Littler, who was on loan from the United Kingdom's Ministry of Supply. When Littler returned to England in 1949, he was succeeded by Carleton Craig from McGill University. It was under him that CARDE was to have its heyday.

With DRB direction, its mandate was expanded into the dawning field of missile research, particularly air-to-air rockets, to equip a new generation of jet aircraft, such as the Canadian-designed-and-built CF100 fighter. At Valcartier, a crash program of building and personnel recruitment was begun, to serve the variety of new roles.

To handle the increased responsibilities, CARDE was divided into five "wings." A Wing was administrative, B dealt with ballistics, C with chemistry (explosives), D with design, and E Wing carried on CARDE's traditional role of trialing and proofing field equipment for the army.

The Liberal government backed up the effort with what it called a "massive funding effort." And, while the researchers employed might have quibbled over its adequacy, money for programs was not the main problem DRB and CARDE faced.

The real difficulty was finding staff who were willing to work for salaries that were far lower than those offered by private industry and foreign research programs. The government and much of its bureaucracy still maintained the conceit that skilled scientists would work cheaply, and out of a sense of national pride. Simply put, they were willing to pay for machinery, but not for the people to build and run it.

When it became obvious that few university graduates wanted to work for "mechanic's wages," the government did nothing to redress the problem. Instead, it attempted to remedy the crisis by raiding the military's officer corps and the university graduate-student programs for personnel.

In speaking of those times, Bull stated that, "the other three guys ahead of me, the '47 class, had all gone to the United States. I was sort of cheesed off because this [the University of Toronto's aeronautical program] was a very forward-looking effort, in developing an advanced-technology institute within the universities...of course, the intent was to have the Canadian graduates come strictly back into Canada; not [to enter into] an international trading ground for exploitation."

According to Captain D. H. Goodspeed, in his 1955 book, *A History of the Defence Research Board of Canada*, "At CARDE there was an establishment for seventy-four professional personnel and three seconded officers, but by the middle of September, 1947, the DRB had been able to employ only eleven suitable professional scientists together with five seconded or attached officers from the Services."

When the DRB decided, in 1950, to go beyond mere research, and undertake its first major development project, the Velvet Glove air-to-air missile, the need for more trained staff became crucial.

The DRB's task was to produce a workable weapon that could be turned over to industry for mass production. Gordon Watson, DRB's best electronics specialist, was put in charge of the general program, plus the specific task of developing the radar-tracking and control system for the missile.

Press reports of the time said his first move was to call Gordon Patterson, and ask him to recommend "a young aerodynamicist, experienced in aerodynamics, hard-working, and with flexible ideas that would allow him to cooperate with scientists working on other branches of the project." They said a youngster was needed, because so few older scientists had any experience in supersonics.

Patterson was supposed to have recommended Gerry, and the scene of him having to convince Watson that his youth and immature looks would not prevent him supervising men much older than himself was again played out.

In 1987, Gerry Bull had a slightly different story to tell. He was to find out what Dr. Solandt's words about ensuring that "the universities produced an adequate flow of well-trained research workers in fields of special interest to defense," meant in practice. He was also to be reminded who was paying his salary.

He claimed he didn't want to go to CARDE at all, preferring to stay at the University of Toronto and finish his doctorate in "a less frenetic environment. What happened was I was summoned; Gordon Patterson summoned me, and I went...and this is a terrifying experience for a young guy, I didn't know what I had done, really. They pointed out that they had a missile project and they needed someone to work on it. I was asked; but it was a gentle suggestion, you know, if I didn't go, the Institute might withdraw my financial support.

"The major deal was, if I went in 1950, providing I came back once a month to Toronto and spent two days a month on the campus, and then did my oral and paperwork, and everything was finished, I just had to publish the thesis [for his Ph.D.]. At that time, there was an international journal for aerophysics, so all I had to do was write it up for that. So, actually, I went in August of 1950 to CARDE. The other condition was 'you can accept no pay'."

Speaking of his Ph.D. work, which would lead to Bull being the youngest person ever to graduate from the University of Toronto with a doctorate, he said, "I really had a year to go before I went to CARDE. I could not leave the [university] program until 1951. I did my Master's in '49, so I had two more years to do my Ph.D. We worked twelve months a year so, by the summer of '50, I was really finished...the rest was just paperwork."

Some have described the ambitious Velvet Glove project as a case of Canada trying to run before it could crawl. The national industrial, technical and information base available at the time would prove to be deficient, in spite of the inspired efforts of men like Gerry Bull. In the end, it became a question of time and cost, as opposed to ability.

Even the project's premise was flawed. The air force felt that, if it had to wait for a perfected British or American missile to be developed, Canada would not be able to produce missiles of its own for years. They thought other nations would concentrate on producing their own first, and would not be able to aid Canada in establishing its own production facilities. They said a Canadian-built missile would, therefore, be available years before one could be produced with foreign aid.

That foreign companies would be eager to profit from assisting Canada in producing versions of their rockets, and could do it without impinging on their own development schedules, didn't occur to the decision makers.

As Bull would later add, "They [the DRB] had no real idea of how much it would cost to develop the missile, or the time it would take to do it...it turned into a real muck-up."

Worse, the range requirement stipulated by the air force turned out to be deficient for combat purposes. Strapped by shortages of all kinds,

Velvet Glove development lagged and, in 1955, the government finally gave up. In March of 1956, it was announced that Canadair of Montréal would produce a licensed version of the American Sparrow air-to-air missile for the air force. Sadly, the Velvet Glove program was to set the standard for much of Canada's further military and civilian technological development efforts.

But that was all in the future, when Gerry Bull bade the LaBrosses farewell at Toronto's Union Station and boarded the train for Québec City. "Aunt Edith cried...Uncle Phil cried, and I cried, too," Bull recalled. "I was leaving home."

Bull's official position at CARDE was Chief Aerodynamicist in B Wing, the ballistics section run by Dr. J.J. "Jimmy" Green. In reality, it was up to him to figure out what the title meant. "Nobody had any idea how I was to accomplish my tasks. I was totally on my own...which I didn't mind a bit," Bull would later say.

Without a paycheck from CARDE, and dependent on his DRB student stipend of less than $3,000 a year, Bull took a third-story room in a cheap but respectable boarding house in Québec City. The tiny room, which was to be his home for the next three years, soon filled up with so many books and file folders that movement became virtually impossible. Abstract mathematical treatises alternated with works of poetry by writers such as Shelley, Byron and particularly Longfellow, who would remain his life-long favorite.

The residence happened to be next door to the spot where General Wolfe had died of his wounds, after his British army had stormed the fortress city, in 1759, and ended French rule in North America. For recreation, the penurious young scientist took to tramping the ancient battlefield, carefully tracing out each action of the struggle.

One of the features of the battle that he found exciting was that, as Wolfe led his flotilla up the St. Lawrence River in the dead of night, past batteries of French cannon, which could have blown them out of the water, he recited Grey's *Elegy In A Country Churchyard*, to maintain his poise. "He was a good judge of poetry," Bull would tell a *Maclean's* writer in 1953. He went on to describe Wolfe "as a rather odd and cultured personality who was difficult to understand intimately."

The writer, Fred Bodsworth, would add this prescient comment. "Bull, a kindred type, would have understood him."

Once again, in later years, Bull took a less sanguine view of these events, and hinted some of it was merely done to relieve his boredom at not being able to have less scholarly outlets. "I couldn't even afford to go to a movie that year," is how he described his existence then. "Looking back now, I don't know how I survived...I was lucky when I could have lunch in the military mess."

Even after he had returned from the University of Toronto in March of 1951, after writing the exam for his Ph.D., the money didn't improve much. "With my Ph.D. done, there was no way the bastards [presumably DRB] could call me a student anymore...they were forced to start paying me a salary, and officially put me on strength."

But, if Bull was being paid starvation wages, the necessity of travelling to the U.S. and the U.K., to confer with allied scientists working on similar projects, meant he had a travel budget. As a member of Canadian scientific delegations, he made numerous trips to Washington, Langley Field, Virginia, New York and San Francisco.

His age and even more youthful looks did not tell against him in discussions with his much-older colleagues. "Gerry knew his stuff," is how one co-worker from CARDE put it. "Three minutes of talking with him and anyone knew that."

"Baby-face," Bull said with good natured resignation, "that's what some people called me in those days. I had a woman come up to me once and ask me if I was waiting for my father. It pissed me off a bit, but it got funny sometimes."

While his good looks and shy smile made him the center of attention for the wives of senior scientists at Washington cocktail parties, Bull was too busy to let it go to his head. Back at CARDE, he was responsible for the aerodynamic design of the Velvet Glove missile, and that presented daunting challenges.

CARDE did not have a wind tunnel, and Bull's efforts to obtain funding for one were dismissed as impractical. For Velvet Glove, he admitted, it would have taken too long to construct, and the University of Toronto facility was already booked far in advance. Even if it had been available, Bull said it lacked the "balances for measuring things," that were required to test an actual missile forebody, instead of a shape set up to see what was involved in shock-wave problems.

In the end, he was forced to do most of the work mathematically, and much of that with pencil and paper. He said they worked "strictly by theory. We were behind, totally behind schedule in 1950 and '51. The thing was, I was completing a Ph.D. as well."

Strangely, it was these problems with a missile program that were to introduce Bull to a field where he would achieve world supremacy—guns and artillery.

"Well, this is how it started. We did theory design, but we didn't have any wind tunnel. We were...about a year and a half away from the first [scheduled] flight test but, gosh, we desperately wanted data. Now, CARDE was an old ballistics establishment, and the guys there suggested, if you can't get any wind-tunnel data why don't you fire a scale model?"

Which is exactly what Bull did. He used an old twenty-five-pounder field gun, and had its barrel rifling removed to make it into a six-inch, smooth-bore cannon. Scale models of the Velvet Glove missile were packed in a sabot, a circular, discardable packing, and fired down a test range at speeds up to 4,500 miles per hour (six times the speed of sound, or Mach 6).

Since the model actually flew, the method was, in many ways, superior to a wind tunnel, where the test shape could not have a complete range of movement, because it was on a pedestal.

As far back as World War II, when the Germans found that high-velocity missiles, such as the V-2, could develop sudden instabilities that caused an otherwise-aerodynamic shape to mysteriously tumble out of control, scientists had sought an answer to the problem.

American theorists had deduced that this was a result of the projectile's pitch (nose up, nose down) movements developing a vibration that, if it reached resonance with a similar frequency in the roll attitude of the missile, would throw it off course and cause it to break up.

At the time, mathematical computations to allow for this pitch and roll instability were so complicated and time-consuming that researchers looked for a simpler method of checking it out. Gerry Bull's lashed-up test range was found to be one of the answers.

The range consisted of a narrow, thousand-foot-long, concrete-block shed, with a sandbagged butt at the far end to catch the spent projectiles. To measure the behavior of the model, several techniques were used, the simplest method being range cards, pieces of paper hung in the projectile's flight path, every ten feet or so, down the length of the tunnel.

As Bull explained, "It [the card idea] originated in England in 1916. They had advanced that type of technique, so that it could do just about anything. We fired the damn things through the cards, and we found when they hit, it left an imprint which would actually give us the angle of attack, so we could measure oscillatory motions just by the yard cards.

"While the technique is consistent, the data-reduction is extremely complicated. Actually, we didn't have computers, we had to compute it manually; but we did it, we got all the aerodynamic derivatives, and that's the only aero-guided missile in history that has ever flown directly from aero-ballistic range data."

While the Velvet Glove missile expired, the cheap and simple solution of Bull's gun range, to the problems of supersonic flight, would live on. Used by a number of friendly foreign governments and other Canadian research projects, it helped keep Canada in the forefront of aerophysical research for over a decade.

The Velvet Glove project also left a useful legacy for both CARDE and Bull. On the material side, CARDE gained assets, such as tracking radars, new test-range facilities and machine shops, that would be useful in other research projects.

Design of the missile had been a cross-disciplinary exercise, involving propulsion, electronics and materials-composition specialists, as well as ballistics experts. The experience and knowledge gained by working in such an environment was, in itself, an education for the scientists and technicians involved. Yet, while it contributed to their skills, it was also, for many, the start of cynicism and despair over the way bureaucracy hampered scientific work.

Project management, and the idea of scientist as executive and decision maker, is not so foreign to us today, but in the early fifties, many in government still perceived scientists as "long-hairs," working in their laboratories on things bureaucrats approved and directed. That only the scientist had the spectrum of knowledge to intelligently make most of the choices, as to what specific directions the work should take, was not understood.

On one hand, the government had defined Velvet Glove as an urgent program, with "the highest priority." On the other, it tied up expenditures in a leisurely web of regulations and approval procedures that left many of the workers fuming.

For Gerry Bull, it was a lesson on the difficulties such projects faced in the real world. He saw research as something one followed with the ardor of a smitten lover. He could not abide those who saw the world as a five-day week. His desire to press on regardless, led him to routinely ignore "established channels," and present his superiors with *faits accomplis* and large bills they had not approved.

"Gerry could never understand people who went home at 4:30 every day," one co-worker from those times said. "He would order concrete to be delivered on Saturdays or Sundays, without regard for other people's schedules. *He was there, why weren't they?* was the way he thought."

Attitudes, which would only harden with the passage of years, were formed in this phase of Bull's career. In 1987, he would refer to bureaucrats as "the lowest form of life on earth." His tactics for dealing with them became a mixture of evasion, deceit, and personal abuse, when his plans were thwarted.

"Gerry said the things we wanted to say, but were afraid to," is how another man put it. "We looked up to him for that."

That there was a tendency for some scientists to become mere time-servers, in such an environment, enraged Bull whenever he thought of it. "What are—what were we there for, except to do science? I couldn't stand guys who just wanted a paycheck. They cheesed me off to no end."

Several times in this period, American research establishments offered Gerry Bull expanded work facilities and higher pay. "Our first offer to you starts at double whatever your pay is now," is how one recruiter began his pitch. Bull turned them all down, and no better comment on the state of his ethics at the time can be found.

The LaBrosses had inoculated him with a strong sense of duty and obligation, in his childhood years. Fully aware of the young Bull's mental gifts, they stressed that a person with intelligence and intellect had a special obligation to use his powers to the limit. The nature of his CARDE duties, and the people he had worked with at the University of Toronto, gave him a strong sense of Canadian nationalism. Combined, the two influences would have a profound effect on his future actions.

By 1953, the twenty-five-year-old Gerry Bull, in spite of his position and scientific accomplishments, was still living an austere life in his cluttered single room in Québec City. The only major purchase he made at the time was to become co-owner of a new Ford coupe, with fellow CARDE employee Dr. Gordon Cann, so they could commute the twenty miles to Valcartier.

Bull also remained a bachelor, with few prospects and seemingly little interest in changing his status. The pace of events at CARDE, interspersed with his working visits to Europe and the United States, left him little time for socializing outside of the scientific community, where the people he met and worked with tended to be at least a decade older than him. The opportunites for meeting unattached women of his age group were strictly limited by circumstances and, even when it happened, Bull generally backed off. A co-worker from those times has described Gerry as "shy and diffident" in the presence of women, and prone to nervous fidgeting when they expressed an interest in him.

One form of recreation Gerry took up was weekend fishing for trout and salmon, in the unspoiled streams pouring into the St. Lawrence River south of Québec City. At the end of one of these trips, in the fall of 1953, a companion informed him that he needed to stop off in the nearby town of Charny, to deliver part of his catch to the house of a prominent local doctor and land-owner, Paul Gilbert.

The doctor's twenty-year-old daughter, Noemi, would remember the visit well. Nicknamed Mimi, "for as long as I can remember," she was a small, slender and vivacious girl, with close-cropped brown hair. At the time, she was attending secretarial college, after having completed grade twelve at a private school in New York City, where she became fluent in English.

She was immediately attracted to Gerry Bull. "I think it was love at first sight," she recalls. "He was slim, with bright blue eyes and lots of curly hair...he had a marvelous smile."

The attraction was mutual, and the usually diffident Gerry Bull went out of his way to charm the young woman. "He had a good sense of humor...he was easy to talk to, and he was very interesting to listen to," she remembers. Gerry suggested that he and his companion take

Mimi and her eighteen-year-old sister, Suzanne, to a play in Québec City the next weekend. Mimi instantly agreed. "Believe it or not, it was a comedy called *Harry the Bunny.*

"I saw him a couple of times after that, and then we didn't see each other until November," Mimi says. (Gerry attended two conferences in the United States that year, and critical pieces of the Velvet Glove program were causing him to work seventy-hour weeks.) "It was at this time I began to discover what he was doing...In the past, he had not talked of his work or the position he held. But we knew we were in love by this time...we got engaged in February of '54."

Mimi's family was dubious about the liaison, at first. She said, "There were mixed feelings, of course, because he was English. It was hard for my parents to get to know him, because Gerry did not speak any French. Later, he did all he could to learn French, and they became the best of friends. He also looked very mature for his age, so they thought he was too old for me."

In light of many people's view that Gerry looked younger than his years, Mimi explained her parents' opinion in terms of what Gerry was doing. "He was far younger than his position would normally call for. When you're talking about the chief of a department, you usually think of someone in his forties."

Gerry invested a great deal of effort, to prove to Dr. Gilbert that he would make a good husband, and the family's objections soon disappeared. Gerry and Noemi were married in Charny's Catholic church on July 15, 1954. The LaBrosses, who were, by this time, living in Montréal, attended the ceremony, and they were the only relatives there. None of Gerry's brothers or sisters even heard of the event until years later.

As a dowry, Dr. Gilbert gave the young couple a "small, but comfortable," house next door to the large and rambling Gilbert mansion in Charny. It was to be their home for the next seven years.

Not that Gerry Bull would see that much of it. From the first, work and travel kept him away for months at a time. Gerry had gone to some lengths to explain the necessity of this to Mimi, even before their engagement, and she accepted it then, as she was to do for the duration of their life together. Two things that made it bearable were Gerry's numerous phone calls, and the long letters that he wrote to her at least once a week. "We were often separated...but we were never apart. Gerry and I loved one another, and that was enough."

Colleagues at CARDE noted the differences married life made in Bull, and say it was a positive change. His somewhat-nerdish and often-frayed style of dress changed to loose, but well-tailored, suits. "Not that Gerry was ever immature in any way, but marriage brought him forward," is how one man put it. "He was quite proud of his family...he had something in his life besides work."

The framework in which that work took place underwent a significant change in the first years of Bull's marriage. By the middle of the 1950s, Canada's government-sponsored scientific-research community had matured and become its own master. In the war years, much of that research had been an adjunct of British science. The large number of "Brits" in leading scientific and administrative positions, at the time, speaks for itself. While the majority worked well with their Canadian colleagues, enough evinced the supercilious attitude that Canada was a colonial backwater, to turn many young, English-descended scientists into incipient nationalists.

With Britain's rapid decline as a world power, in the 1950s, came the end of Canadian research projects headed by Cambridge graduates. The "Canadianization" of the country's science community was welcomed by a generation of young, educated men, who saw it as contributing to the emergence of "a true north, strong and free."

"Gerry always believed in Canadian science, done in Canada, by Canadians," is how a CARDE associate defined it. This is not to say that Bull disdained cooperation with other countries—far from it. But, like his co-workers and most of his immediate superiors, he believed it had to be from a strong and effective national base, which had something to offer to other nations.

By the end of his first five years at CARDE, some tarnish was appearing on the high ideals. Perhaps it was a justifiable cynicism, for Bull was learning about the "real world" in which scientists doing government research had to work. It was more than bureaucrats slowing things down with paperwork. Bull was beginning to see the role of politicians in Canadian scientific projects.

In a Canada at peace that was striving for a consumer-oriented society, elected representatives showed few signs of truly appreciating what science was about. Captain Goodspeed, in his book on the DRB, said that Canada, in the early 1950s, had traded development of a homegrown industrial base for a quick supply of foreign cars, stoves and refrigerators. While it is easy to accuse the political leadership of a cynical desire to win votes, by spreading quick prosperity to a society tired of making sacrifices, the failing was actually worse than that. It was an inability to understand the critical role of science and technology in a modern nation's strength and unity, and what they required to prosper.

Much as they promoted the idea of "Canadian science," in speeches to professional associations, the politicians did not see that scientific development, by itself, is a sterile exercise. Science needs to be used. Research and development that cannot lead to the production of products or technologies, whether military or civilian, is a waste. Yet, the idea that Canadian science would need Canadian industry to deploy its discoveries, didn't hammer through. What use did General Motors or Nabisco Brands have for Canadian science?

While Bull's description of Canadian Members of Parliament as "second-rate lawyers and jumped-up real-estate salesmen" can be dismissed as his normal hyperbole, the fact that lawyers form the largest professional group in politics bears scrutiny, since they are perhaps the most technically illiterate of all the professions. Today, when people as different as Conrad Black and David Suzuki point out the paradox of a technically-advanced society being run by those who have precious little knowledge of even the most basic scientific principles, the problem gets more talk, if little action.

Gerry Bull put the situation bluntly. "I came across cab drivers in Montréal who understood more about what we were doing at CARDE than some of our goddamned Liberal cabinet ministers."

Nor, as Bull was to ruefully find out, did they have any interest in learning. There is a story that Bull spent part of an inter-departmental meeting, in 1965, trying to explain his work to C.M. "Bud" Drury, minister for both the industry and defense-production portfolios between 1965 and 1969. Increasingly frustrated, as the politician could not, or would not, grasp what he was saying, he finally threw down his notes and told the man he had "the technical competence of a baboon." Under the horrified gazes of the other participants, he then stomped out of the room.

The tale typifies Bull's attitude toward politicians. The fact that he didn't hide his attitudes began to tell against him, where funding was involved. An amorphous collection of senior scientists, administrators and Members of Parliament, which Bull described as "my enemies," began to form. The idea that there was any real "Get Bull" movement is discounted by most. On the other hand, they will admit there "were a lot of people who didn't like Gerry Bull."

In an environment where politicians controlled the purse-strings, and took careful note of which province and what riding the money was spent in, Bull's acknowledged brilliance would only protect him so far.

CHAPTER 5

Not long after his marriage, Gerry Bull received several pay raises, as the government played partial catch-up on the salaries of its scientists. Combined with the ownership of the house in Charny, it brought him, if not affluence, then a least a more comfortable style of living. Here the role of his new wife's family and their fortune must be factored in, since it was to have an increasing role in Bull's career.

Like his father, Gerry had married into a wealthy French-Canadian family and, though love was undoubtedly the attraction, with gifts like a house, it could not help but favorably affect his finances. Mimi Bull is reluctant to discuss what she calls "our personal finances." She says her father, Paul Gilbert, was "not wealthy, but comfortable." However, long-term residents of Lauzom county, where Charny is located, all described the Gilbert family as "rich and very influential."

Behind the backdrop of work, high-level conferences and national press coverage, Bull studiously kept his new family life as divorced as possible from the world outside. Mimi Bull remembers that, from the first, he saw his home as a refuge "from the press of events," and that "he seldom brought the office home."

On July 3, 1955, the refuge gained another member when Mimi gave birth to the couple's first son, Philippe. As with all the seven children they were to have, Gerry made sure he was there for the event, regardless of his work or travel schedules. Mimi Bull recalls him being a "typically nervous first-time father...but he was immensely pleased with the result." He must have been, for the next year the Bull's repeated the experience and had a second son, Michel, in November.

That year, the proud, new father watched, as a series of management changes took place above him at the Defence Research Board. Dr Solandt, who had been head of what was referred to as "the fourth branch of the nation's defense machine," retired and accepted a job as a vice-president of Canadian National Railways. While his salary doubled with this move (from $17,500 to $35,000), some have said his leaving was "suggested" by the government. His increasingly outspoken public statements on the horrors of nuclear war, and what he saw as the need to spend more on defensive research against atomic weapons, disturbed both the politicians and an increasingly large segment of the population, who wanted less spending on defense, not more.

A medical doctor who graduated from the University of Toronto with the highest marks in the school's history, Solandt started his career in military research when he became director of the physiological laboratory of the British Army's armored fighting-vehicle school, during World War II. Later, with the rank of brigadier in the Canadian army, he was scientific adviser to Lord Louis Mountbatten. At the conflict's end, he served as a member of the Allied Military Mission, which went to Japan to investigate the effects of the atomic bombing of Hiroshima and Nagasaki. The sheer scope of the destruction had a profound effect on Solandt. More quickly than most scientists of his time, he began to comprehend that atomic bombs were not just another weapon.

His replacement was A. Hartley Zimmerman, a geologist and mining engineer who was director-general of Canadian communications production during the war. Joining the DRB in 1951, as director of the electronics division, he rose quickly in the administrative ranks before his appointment as chairman.

If the job was a major goal, it was to be a Pyrrhic victory. Defense spending in Canada, as a percentage of the gross national product, would steadily decline as the decade grew older. Deprived of Solandt's prestige, and the intimate knowledge of the government's power structures gained during his eight-year tenure, DRB's importance as a vehicle for research funding slowly declined. CARDE, because of its relatively large share of the DRB research pie, was to suffer the most and bear it longer.

Carleton Craig, who had done so much to get CARDE and its scientists up and running during his three years as superintendent, had been replaced in 1952 by Dr. H.M. Barret, who stayed until his appointment as Chief of Establishments for the DRB in 1955. He was followed by a man who, within the confines of Ottawa's political and bureaucratic intrigues, would become somewhat controversial for his association with Gerry Bull—Brigadier D.A.G. "Doug" Waldock.

Opinions vary widely on the man. Some who worked at CARDE under his administration have dismissed him as a "duffer" and a "pompous office soldier." Others, while admitting he was less knowledgeable in science than the man he replaced, say he was a competent administrator, who supported his scientists to the limit of his powers and took a genuine interest in what they were doing.

Some idea of CARDE's importance as a center of DRB research can be gained by looking at where DRB's personnel were deployed. Once considered a state secret, the numbers were first released in 1957, when DRB had a total of 2,800 employees, 1,320 of whom were scientific or technical personnel. CARDE employed over 1,000 of the total staff, some 400 of them being scientists and technicians.

Located thirty kilometers northwest of Québec City, on a remote twenty-four thousand acres of low hills and scrub pine, CARDE was a place where security has been described as "tight, but unobtrusive...if there had been infiltrators, it would have been a toss-up to see who got them first, the guards or the mosquitoes."

Dominated by the long, low, thousand-foot structure of the enclosed ballistic range, where Gerry Bull fired his projectiles, the main work area was an untidy sprawl of barracks, machine shops and administrative structures, in either wood or utilitarian concrete block. In the faded pictures of those days, there is a raw, transient look to it all. It fits the image of an organization that, for all its accomplishments, was struggling to survive.

As Gerry Bull put it, "We lived from hand to mouth at CARDE. We never knew from one month to the other if we'd be there the next." Speaking of his own projects, he said, "Six times, the bastards canceled us...six times, we got reprieves at the last moment."

Increasingly, "the bastards" were a federal ministry then known as Trade and Commerce. Its role in financing scientific research rose, as the DRB's status declined. Funding issues were also to become more complex and time-consuming for the scientists themselves.

The picture presented, to date, of Bull and his experimental work, as a DRB effort, can be misleading, in that it ignores how most scientific research is funded and carried out in Western countries. Project money usually comes from a variety of government, institutional and industry sources, no matter who is administering the show on paper. To further complicate it, personnel-trading between research organizations means the workers may wear a wide variety of hats, and conduct their specific experimentation in other institutions or private companies. Thus, an organization like the National Research Council (NRC), dedicated to civilian-oriented research, had several scientists seconded to CARDE in the fields of aerophysical research, and employees of companies like Canadian Westinghouse were on hand at Valcartier.

Especially on the funding side, many have criticized this *ad hoc* approach, saying that the successful scientist is often the one who can effectively shill his ideas to different audiences, and count on friends and influence to get his way. Yet the method does have its advantages. For the contributors, it ensures a failed effort will not have wasted an entire budget, and it allows the taking of chances by spreading the risk. Besides, as supporters point out, blarney will get one only so far, and a good idea will often be picked up on and supported for its merit alone.

One truism about this scientific marketplace is that there will always be more ideas than available money. In such a competitive situation, even the best have to hustle, and Gerry Bull was no exception. In spite of his professed contempt for "cocktail scientists," who spent their time politicking for funds, Bull played as good a game of it as anyone. He was beginning to behave with a roughneck insensitivity to competitors, which won on points, but built resentments that would surface in later years, when those who were slighted held positions of authority in the academic and governmental hierarchies.

Bull complained about the way he was funded, and how the "dread phrase, 'approved in principle' meant nothing if you didn't get the money on time." He claimed, "Like, OK, they'd give us X dollars for that fiscal year, and then we'd get it in the last three months of the year...how could we work that way?"

Recently retired from Ottawa's Carlton University, Professor Jack Templin spent much of his career with the NRC, and worked at Valcartier with Bull in the late 1950s. He laughed, when presented with Bull's version of his funding problems. "That was Gerry's own budgeting; that was one of his methods, you know...He'd get all these things going towards the end of a budget, and then he'd turn around and say, 'You wouldn't dare, how could you kill a thing when we're just getting so much out of it. Oh sure, we used up the money, but you really didn't give us enough in the first place.' Then he'd ask for more. So his method, even at CARDE, was to do as much as he could first, and then ask permission."

CARDE's need for a wind tunnel had not diminished with Bull's use of gun systems for aerodynamic research. Repeatedly balked in a search for funding, he decided, in 1954, that any type of tunnel would be better than none at all. In a small-scale repeat of his University of

Toronto experience, he put a team of graduate students to work on building "a large scale model," while turning the experience into a part-time course on advanced aerodynamics for the participants, under the aegis of Laval University in Québec City.

Capable of operating at Mach 4 (3,000 mph), the tunnel went into operation in the summer of 1955, and cost just $6,000, which is not surprising, considering that most of the installation was scrounged natural-gas storage tanks (for the vacuum chamber) and "creative welding in the machine shops."

"Scrap....we did most of our work at CARDE with scrap...scrap gun barrels, scrap equipment, you name it." Bull would later say.

As the 1953, "Jerry [sic] Bull, Boy Rocket Scientist" *Maclean's* article showed, Gerry had already discovered the role the media could play in advancing scientific research in general, and his work in particular. Having a knack for painting science in terms simple enough for newspaper reporters to understand, he got headlines on more than one occasion.

"UNVEIL CANADIAN GUN THAT FIRES 4,550 M P H MISSILES," read the headline of the May 20, 1955, Toronto *Telegram*. In a story that drew national attention, and was released with the full approval of his superiors, Bull's hitherto-secret work was revealed in front-page detail, as an example of Canada's new ranking in the field of science. Reporters were discovering that Gerry Bull made good copy, and more, was a man who took the time to explain things in a simple, sensible way that could be transmitted to a large audience. His obvious commitment and enthusiasm for what he was doing came through.

Yet, behind the press coverage of past achievements, Bull had come up with another, simple, brilliant idea that was to have a profound effect on his career. It was a logical extension of his gun-fired-models technique. Observing free-flying models by photographic or range card means was effective, but limited in scope.

As Bull put it, "The idea was, why couldn't we put in telemetry? [i.e., a radio to send back sensor information from the model itself] There were radar-type fuses in W.W. II, which was electronics in a shell, and now we had transistors, so it seemed rather obvious to me that we should be able to do something; it was opposed very violently by the conventional electronic people...everyone said 'It's impossible.' It's the story of my life."

Biased by their previous experiences with fragile vacuum-tube technology, many scientists with DRB and the NRC claimed that even radios built with the new solid-state devices would never stand the shock of a gun launch. They dismissed it as another wild Bull idea, and recommended against funding and development.

Bull was to quickly prove the doubters wrong, by doing another end run around established procedures. On his own authority, he declared the matter an internal, B Wing decision, and shuffled his funding. "I had my own division then, so I hired my own electronics staff. We found that, pretty soon, we could put in all the telemetry and frequency modulation that we wanted. We built the transmitter, and simply cast it into epoxy. So, after this, when we were firing in the range, we had instrumented models and were receiving the data, which, incidently, was presented at the Seventh Annual American Aeronautical Conference in New York...it was presented throughout the world."

For Bull, the success of the instrumented test-range firings was a revelation with broad implications. "I could basically say I don't need a ballistic range anymore." Once it's out of the gun muzzle, it's identical to a rocket-launch vehicle; it's carrying it's own instrumentation. This was our first inspiration in seeing the gun as a complimentary device; that was around 1957-'58."

Bull's contention that, compared to rockets, gun-launched projectiles could be a cheaper and more reliable means of conducting scientific research in the upper atmosphere and beyond, produced much acclaim in the international aeronautical community, but no support in Canada. Just one organization saw the concept's promise, and was willing to provide money, staff and technical support. For Bull, it was the beginning of an association with the American army, and with two men who not only believed in his work, but were to become his firmest friends. In future times, when many others were to suddenly distance themselves from Gerry Bull, they remained his staunchest supporters. To this day, they still defend his memory.

As Bull described it, "...at that time, there was a gentleman called Lieutenant General Arthur G. Trudeau...he came up to CARDE and he said, 'I don't really believe what you're doing here.'"

Described as "a very intellectual man," in contrast to the outlooks of many army officers, Trudeau was attracted to the elementary simplicity of Bull's ideas. Bull's enthusiasm and technical brilliance also exercised a personal attraction on this scholarly warrior, which was to make their relationship more than science or business.

One of the institutions under Trudeau's command, during his tenure as Chief of U.S. Army Research and Development, was the Aberdeen Proving Ground. Established in 1918, on what was then a remote site northeast of Baltimore, Maryland, Aberdeen provided the theoretical and testing component of the U.S. army's artillery forces in peace and war. The Ballistics Research Laboratory (BRL) of Aberdeen matched CARDE's B Wing, and Dr. Charles Murphy was Bull's opposite number. In the arcane world of ballistic research, the two were to be a match in drive, age and intellect.

As Gerry Bull recalled those early days of HARP, "Charlie Murphy and his group got instructions to get together, and they built the five-inch gun, and put in the telemetry, and they did the first firing with the little five-inch in 1961."

This smooth-bore device was located on the Edgewood peninsula, seventeen miles from the center of Baltimore. Here, the BRL fired instrumented shells that reached a maximum altitude of 130,000 feet. Observed by a modified Nike Hercules missile-fire-control radar, the probes deployed clouds of aluminum-foil chaff to test shell-tracking concepts, as well as proving the utility of gun-fired scientific devices.

The gun-launched instrument concept was only one of Bull's interests, at the time. His responsibilities at CARDE increased dramatically during the late fifties. Besides overseeing his department's conduct of aerophysical research for a variety of Canadian and international organizations, he was also involved in the biggest technical effort that Canada would ever attempt, the Avro Arrow jet project.

The February, 1959, cancellation of the Arrow, by the Conservative government of John Diefenbaker, is the best-known example of Canada's repeated failures in the field of advanced technology. While the demise of Velvet Glove, the Bras D'or hydrofoil, the Bobcat armored personnel carrier, and a host of smaller efforts remain unknown, except to a small group of technical aficionados, the Arrow still attracts controversy and interest, thirty years later. Seldom a year goes by without another book or television show on the subject. The heat and emotion generated by the decision, and the public's continuing interest in the debacle, show a general awareness that something more than an airplane passed away.

The debate as to whether the Arrow would have been a viable aircraft, for the role of a long-range bomber-interceptor, designed to fit a mid-1950s idea of how a global nuclear war would be fought, still rages. But, tales of cost overruns and problems with senior management aside, the political decision to end the Arrow was perhaps the most inept move by the federal government in the past fifty years.

In his 1979 book, *Fall of an Arrow*, author Murray Peden defined it with these stark and simple words. "The effect was to dash the struggling Canadian aircraft and engine industry from its proud position as temporary leader of the western world....and relegate it, almost instantly, to the outermost boondocks of the industrial minor leagues."

The words are not an exaggeration. In the early 1950s, American aviation designers saw Canada as a friendly and cooperative nation, with much to offer in the latest technologies. The companies they worked for perceived their northern neighbor as a potential major competitor in the world aircraft market.

How many Canadians today know that their nation, in 1949, produced the Avro Jetliner, the first North American commercial jet transport, or that it once built state-of-the-art fighter planes, such as the

CF-100, which American air force generals publicly envied? American corporate policies that demanded their government purchase only "homegrown" aircraft were to combine with Canadian stupidity, to turn it all into historical dust.

The Arrow project attracted the brightest and best of Canadian scientific and engineering talent, in government, university and private industry. It was a skills and knowledge base of impressive dimensions, which was to be callously dissipated. Worse than cancelling the Arrow itself, the government had no plan, no field of endeavor in which to utilize the human resources assembled by fifteen years of concerted effort. Almost the entire Canadian aerospace community, twenty-nine thousand men and women of exceptional talent, were rendered redundant. The effect was to leave these people with no place to go except the United States, where the "Canadian content" of NASA's Apollo moon landings was to be lost in the footnotes of scholarly journals.

As might be expected, Gerry Bull and CARDE had an important role to play in the development of the Arrow. An aircraft that pushed aeronautical development into new fields of practical, supersonic flight required extensive preliminary testing, to see if the radical new ideas on wing shape and engine-inlet geometry that the designers proposed, actually worked.

CARDE and Bull's gun-fired projectile system was ideal for much of this work. Jack Templin, then head of the NRC's Aerodynamics Laboratory, recalls the time well. He was responsible for aerodynamic studies of the Arrow's performance and stability envelope. This led to a close association with Gerry Bull, and some innovative solutions to accomplishing their work.

As Templin put it, "Gerry had this idea of firing model aircraft [out of guns], and it really interested me. There's an advantage in using a gun and a free-flying model...wind tunnel models are held still, so you can't effectively measure a lot of things. This was why he wanted to be able to fire model aircraft."

There is some dispute over where the idea came from. Templin recalls that "Gerry seemed to think he was the first person to actually do this...but its not quite clear. He worked so closely with Charlie Murphy that I think he got the idea at the same time, or maybe Charlie had the same idea, or maybe he got it from Gerry...we'll never know. Anyway, Gerry said Charlie was going to try to beat him to firing the first model aircraft, down at Aberdeen. He took it as a challenge.

"Gerry hadn't the time to prepare the first Arrow models for the range, so he went out and bought some Dinky Toys. One of them was the little English fighter, a delta-wing fighter that looked vaguely like the Arrow, but it was an earlier one, the Gloucester Javelin. It was a subsonic airplane, anyway. He fired that down the range and took his shadowgraph/photograph of it, which outlined the shock-waves, showing the flow field...Anyway, you could tell from that the thing was going supersonic.

"He sent the picture to Charlie, to let him know he was beat, and afterwards he wondered what to do with it. He got looking at this picture, and he thought the Meccano Company, the people who make Dinky Toys, might like to see this. So he sent it over to them with a note explaining it, and they used it for a while in the Dinky Toy ads."

With the concept proven by the Dinky Toy firings, Bull set to work with proper Arrow models, to assist the designers in testing the design values. Shot after shot went down the range, yielding confirmation of the Arrow's advanced geometry. As Timpkin remembers, "At that time, there were some questions about the stability of the Avro Arrow. We had done wind tunnel tests, and Gerry was determined to do the range firing, and that was done at one of the ballistic ranges at CARDE."

One of the challenges Bull and Templin faced was that the Avro Arrow was perhaps the first aircraft in the world to even partially dispense with what designers call arrow-stability. This refers to the ability of an aircraft to maintain its heading, without moving control surfaces. The rear feathers on an arrow give the stick this feature; hence the name. While aircraft with arrow-stability are safe-to-fly designs, it causes a lot of drag, so most modern fighter planes today dispense with it, in whole or in part. They are deliberately unstable, and use computer systems to maintain heading and attitude.

According to Templin, "The Arrow had one characteristic like that, it really arose accidentally, but it had directional instability....You could think of it as the tail fin not being big enough. The company was determined to fix it all up electronically, which wasn't exactly the safest thing to do in those days....even they [fly-by-wire-systems] don't fix up the complete static stability, they fix up the dynamic stability...but the Arrow had a little more peculiar problem than that. Of course, it was flown, but without the assistance of the electronic system. The flight tests were planned to avoid any areas where they might get into that trouble. A lot of attention was paid to the stability of it, and that was Gerry's contribution to the Arrow."

While Bull's portion of the Arrow development was done by the time of the government's decision, he shared the horror, anger and frustration of the entire aerospace community. His distaste for technically illiterate politicians and bureaucrats rose to new heights. Indeed, Bull would give the Arrow fiasco as one of his main reasons for eventually leaving CARDE.

On October 4, 1957, something happened, on the far side of the world, that would have a profound affect on Gerry Bull and just about every other aerophysical scientist in North America. That day the Soviet Union stunned the world, with the launching of Sputnik, the first artificial satellite. The twenty-three-inch-diameter sphere with its protruding whip antennas was a slap in the face for the United States and its allies, who had always assumed their technological superiority over the Soviet bloc.

Heightened by the blusterings of Nikita Khrushchev over the progress of "communist technology," and its prominent place in the upcoming "world victory of socialism," many in the West took fright. As American Vanguard satellite rockets blew up on their launch pads, it seemed, to scientists and laymen alike, that mysterious Russia had suddenly become a technological giant. That most of it was bluff and without substance—we now know there never was a missile gap—didn't matter, in the context of the times. All over the Western world, scientists looked for ways to counter Soviet accomplishments and restore the prestige of the "decadent, capitalist West."

Six months after the launch of Sputnik, *The Toronto Star* of April 22, 1958, carried the four-inch banner headline: **CANADA HAS MOON**—Send Up Own Satellite This Year. The copyrighted story began:

> Canadian scientists plan to launch an earth satellite this year, it has been learned from an unimpeachable source.
>
> The source, who asked not to be identified, revealed in an exclusive interview with The Star that the satellite is being readied by scientists of the Defence Research Board's Canadian armament research and development establishment at Valcartier, Quebec.
>
> If all goes according to present plans, the Canadian baby moon—-a radio-equipped plastic sphere six inches in diameter and weighing about two pounds—-will be launched late this summer or in the fall.

It was an amazing, if wildly inaccurate, piece of journalism, and the "unimpeachable source" was Gerry Bull. The space project, as the *Star* described it, was certainly original.

> An ingenious method of putting satellites into orbit has been devised by a team of young researchers under brilliant, Toronto-born Dr. Gerry V. Bull...it consists of marrying an oxygen-hydrogen gun now being built at the Valcartier research centre, to a U.S.-produced Redstone ballistic missile.
>
> The Canadian army will begin training with these missiles—they stand almost 70 feet high and

can attain an altitude of 150 miles—this summer, and has agreed to allow the scientists to use one of these rockets to carry the gun and satellite above most of the earth's atmosphere.

The 15-foot oxygen-hydrogen gun, expected to be ready in June, will be sunk into the rocket's nose. Once the rocket has reached a predetermined altitude and angle, an explosion of the two gases will propel the little moon into space at an acceleration of about 1,000,000 Gs.

There was no Canadian plan to launch satellites, and the Canadian army was not receiving Redstone missiles. Feasible or not—and even scientists who still admire Bull give the idea a laugh and a "well, maybe," at best—one vein of opinion claims it was all in Gerry's head. He had taken a concept and presented it as a reality without informing any of his superiors. Others were to say he was used by a reporter out for a sensational scoop, a man who had taken Bull's speculations and presented them as truth.

Whichever way, the morning after the *Star* article, Prime Minister John Diefenbaker emerged from the House of Commons in Ottawa, and was besieged by a horde of reporters wanting to know about "the Canadian moon." Diefenbaker just stared at them for a moment, then laughed and said, "You're not really serious?"

Informed that they were, the Prime Minister retreated for a moment, and grabbed the nearby Defence Minister, George Peakes, for a whispered conference. Returning to the press scrum, he reported back that "There is no foundation whatsoever to the story...not a scintilla of truth in it."

As the day progressed, senior appointees in the chain of responsibility issued their own statements of denial and, in turn, demanded of their subordinates what the hell was going on. Charles King, of Southam News, described it "as the biggest flap at Ottawa defense headquarters since the horses-on-the-payroll scandals at Petawawa, Ontario, in 1952."

The closer to the source of the controversy, the hotter the questions got. Even though he had issued a denial, which was printed in the original *Star* article, Brigadier Waldock, along with Bull's immediate superior, John Green, ended up on the carpet. "Its fair to say it caused them a lot of trouble and embarrassment," is how a present-day senior scientist with the NRC described it.

Why Bull did it—if, indeed, he actually had—will never be known, but some scientists who knew him then have speculated that he was driven by his increasing frustrations to "maybe try and kickstart the government into doing something, anything, in the field of rocket science."

By April 24, the controversy had subsided to back-page articles that no longer referred to Bull as brilliant, but as a "junior scientist." By the end of the week it was gone.

But not entirely forgotten. "In a bureaucracy, such things are remembered years hence, and can be ammunition against you—they [Waldock and Green] must have hated Gerry for putting them on the spot like that, and I don't know if I blame them. What Gerry did was way out of line...it was nutty," is how one ex-NRC man described the incident.

Along with a growing reputation for getting angry with people who didn't see it his way, Bull's moon story left many in government with the impression this driven, complex man was not very stable. Those who didn't like him took comfort in that and, for Gerry Bull, the Ottawa climate took on a distinct and lasting chill.

Jack Templin made a good point when he said that, in talking of Bull's enemies, one first ought to look at who his friends were.

"I think they were all people who were sort of like himself, people who were doing that same kind of work. For instance, there used to be a certain amount of unfriendliness, shall we say, between Defence Research Board, which he worked for, and NRC among certain things, but not at the working level. So, for instance, on the Arrow, there was cooperation between the two. Also, at an earlier date, at CARDE they helped them develop the Velvet Glove missile. And Gerry was involved with the project...there was a lot of to-ing and fro-ing between NRC and CARDE at that time.

"As to his enemies, well, the people that I know best were associated with Gerry, and there aren't very many of them left. They were all people on the scientific side: I don't think they ever fell into Gerry's enemy camp... one thing; if you ever did, you knew it. Anything to do with bureaucracy, whether it was at CARDE or DRB HQ, he hated. He considered DRB HQ to be sort of an enemy camp. They did nothing but damp the works, as far as he was concerned, 'cause, of course, most of the things he wanted to do he would have to seek permission from Headquarters, but the names of the people, I don't know...."

It was inevitable that Bull's days at CARDE were numbered, not so much by the efforts of others as by his own realization that it was leading him nowhere. For all the work he had done, there was no reward or feeling of accomplishment. What good was brilliant effort on canceled projects? Gerry Bull wanted to succeed by his own definition of the word, and he finally saw that CARDE was not the place to do it. "I got sick of butting my head against the wall with those guys," he would later say.

As with many of Bull's major decisions in life, his leaving CARDE might have been motivated by long evolved conclusions, but it came suddenly, and without much thought, on April 1, 1961.

Questioned regarding the dramatic circumstances surrounding Bull's departure, Jack Templin laughed again. "It depends who you ask. It would seem that he left CARDE by mutual consent, according to a lot of people. Gerry told me that he resigned on the spot when he was called into the superintendent's office...a man named Johnny Green, Dr. J.J. Green. I guess he was one of Gerry's silent enemies. Johnny's dead now. He worked in various government departments for a while. He was in the air force during the war. He was at NRC before I ever went there; later he was at the Department of Transport.

"Anyway, he got into trouble with the superintendent over some sort of paperwork. I don't know what it was; Gerry was never bothered with paperwork. He told me that he got called up by the Superintendent and they got into an argument, and Gerry finally said to him, 'Which is more important, paperwork or getting the work done?' and he said 'In this case, the paperwork.' So Gerry said 'You want paperwork? I'll give you paperwork!' He wrote out his resignation there on the spot."

A Canadian army intelligence summary, prepared after Bull's death and obtained under the Canadian Access to Information Act, offers this view of the incident. "...his tempestuous nature and strong dislike for administration and red tape constantly led him into trouble with senior management. After being reprimanded and chastised for not abiding by the rules, Bull left DRB and became a Professor of Engineering Science at McGill in 1961."

CHAPTER 6

In 1961, Montréal's McGill University was an Anglo island in a French sea, an institution curiously isolated from its own time. Stiff pictures of faculty members in English tweeds, and class photos of neatly clothed males interspersed with a rare, demurely dressed young woman, come from the late 1950s and early '60s, but there is an older, almost 1930s, charm about them. Before the backdrops of Union Jacks and the thin-framed pictures of dead kings, McGill presented an image of WASPness, a serene sense of Anglo-Saxon-Celtic cultural permanence. Yet the paradox was that, however conservative it might have seemed, McGill was more amenable to taking chances on science and technology than any other educational institution in Canada. It was, uniquely, a place that would listen to the radical if he had sufficient brilliance.

Nowhere was this more evident than in the engineering faculty, headed by Dean Donald L.Mordell. An honors graduate of Cambridge University, he had worked at the Rolls Royce research laboratories in Derby, England, during World War II, and played an important role in the development of the gas turbine engine that powered Britain's first jet fighter.

As with the University of Toronto, the war-driven rush to advance science and technology had irrevocably changed McGill. When Mordell arrived with his new Master's degree, in the fall of 1947, to take up a position as an associate professor of mechanical engineering, he came to an institution that had expanded in both size and outlook. According to Dr. F. Cyril James, then principal and vice-chancellor of McGill, "Members of the instructional staff now total 894, as compared with 473 in the 1938-39 session...on the other hand, the student body has nearly tripled. It is expected to be 8,200 in the approaching season."

Four thousand of those students were war veterans, men whose experiences had made them older than their years. Their outlooks tended to be tough, pragmatic and "solution oriented." At a time when Mordell could sketch a future world tied together by the sleek jet transports we now take for granted, they listened to the dream and got to work on making it reality.

While it was Mordell's scientific work, particularly his research in the new Gas Dynamics Laboratory from 1948 to 1958, that made his reputation, it was his skills as an administrator and coordinator that led to his 1954 appointment as department chairman, and later to the post of Dean of Faculty, in 1957.

Perhaps the most dramatic illustration of Mordell's belief that theoretical knowledge must be backed by practical experiences was his decision, in 1953, to obtain his pilot's license, the first known case of a Canadian university dean to do so.

Volume Two of Stanley Brice Frost's *History of McGill University* sums up his career as follows: "Beginning with his own department, he was able, partly through fortunate circumstances but also by reason of his own enthusiasm and energy, to encourage a new mood of optimism in the faculty as a whole. He was fortunate that J.G. Notman and J.R. McLagen, graduates of the Mechanical Engineering Department and governors of the university, had seen the need to establish a fund to re-equip the department with the machinery and instruments required in its fast developing field."

Such was the institution that Gerry Bull came to, with his plans for a major Canadian presence in space research, using big guns. In June of that year, he was appointed Professor of Mechanical Engineering, and took up offices in the department's building on Woodland Circle, in the Montréal suburb of St.Bruno. While he would conduct some postgraduate classes in gas and fluid dynamics for a half-dozen students, his main task was to be research.

The sudden move to Montréal involved the Bulls selling their house in Charny, and quickly finding a new home close to the university. The shift was complicated by the birth of the Bull's fourth son, Richard, the previous April. While Gerry was once more there for the delivery, his young wife was discovering how his frequent absences were increasing her responsibilities for raising their growing brood. In her words, "He was not always available for the bringing up of the children...I became used to long separations."

The family's house-hunting was aided by the fact that Bull's posting as a full professor brought a considerably higher salary than he had been receiving at CARDE. After some searching, they found what they considered to be "a dream home" in St. Bruno. Wide lawns and tall hedges surrounded a large, turn-of-the-century stone structure that remains Mimi's home to this day.

While the job was new, Bull was not a stranger to the McGill engineering faculty. Geography and mutual needs had insured long-standing links between CARDE and McGill. In fields as diverse as gunnery-range instrumentation, radar, electronics and rocket motors, McGill had provided scientific know-how and instrument assembly, for programs like the Velvet Glove air-to-air missile. In return, it received scientific data acquired by CARDE, and an "operational insight" into what directions its scientific and engineering scholarship should follow in the future.

It was logical, then, that Mordell and Bull should form a growing relationship in the 1950s. Much of CARDE's research works were really Bull's initiatives and, according to one of Mordell's students at the time, "...he gained a deep and lasting impression of Gerry's abilities, when he was at Valcartier."

This faith in Bull was to stand the test of time. For almost a decade, Mordell remained one of his staunchest supporters. He seldom missed an opportunity to explain the importance of Bull's work to anyone in government and industry who would listen.

This is not to say he was uncritical, or any sort of worshiper. Bull's occasional displays of histrionics, and what one person from the CARDE days described as his "second-rate attempts at manipulation," often dismayed his supporters. "[Mordell] always supported Bull's work...I think sometimes he got pretty tired of having to defend Bull." is how a one-time McGill professor put it.

Bull's arrival at McGill marked the start of a high-profile research effort in gun-launched projectiles, which would win fame as the High Altitude Research Projectile (HARP). Bull would later describe his association with the university as "a marriage made in heaven." Freed of the bureaucratic strictures of the DRB, he was far more in control of his own work, and was able to plan for the future with some degree of confidence. Not only was he able to tap the academic resources of McGill, and a considerable amount of in-house funding for HARP, but his close association with Aberdeen's Charles Murphy and Lieutenant General Trudeau brought funding and logistical support from the U.S. army. His connections with the University of Toronto were another source of financial, scientific and instrumentation assistance.

Thus, Project HARP came into being, as a complex endeavor involving many institutions. While McGill can be seen as "the owner of record," HARP, in practice, was beholden to no one institution or country. Since Murphy and Bull were soon established as co-equal technical directors, the cooperative and international flavor of the first phases of HARP are clear.

As Gerry Bull pointed out in 1988, the research was divided into two phases. First, there was an entire engineering and research operation to develop the gun-launch systems. Secondly, there were programs to develop experiments that could make use of the gun technology. As Bull put it, "In each of those engineering research and development fields, we built up quite substantial working groups of our own. We also built up a very large group of specialists in American industry, especially in electronic-related fields."

When it came time to select the HARP test and development sites, Bull had a personal contribution to make. Several years before, Gerry and Mimi had bought an isolated, two-thousand-acre bloc of rolling, forested hills, near the hamlet of Highwater on the Québec-Vermont border, some sixty miles southeast of Montréal. Donated for the use of the project, the property would grow over the years, as McGill purchased several adjoining blocks of land, until the plot stretched to the American border and encompassed over four thousand acres.

The site provided space for a new ballistics range and test facility. Under the energetic direction of Robert Stacey, a retired colonel from the British army who was appointed Highwater Station General Manager, roads were bulldozed, power lines run in, and a series of rough wood buildings constructed to house on-site activities. Machine shops, bunk houses, adminstration offices and instrumentation structures were soon in place.

Yet the ambitious scope of HARP required test sites far beyond Highwater, Québec. In addition to the use of Aberdeen's facilities, and those of the American army in Arizona, McGill gave Bull access to a location of far greater potential.

For two decades, McGill had been running climatic and agricultural research stations on the Caribbean island of Barbados. The university's close connections with the fledgling Democratic Labour Party (DLP) government of the newly emerging nation gave Bull the opportunity to explain his needs to senior government officials. He gained the enthusiastic support of Prime Minister Errol W. Barrow, and was given use of a piece of land near Foul Bay, on the southeast corner of the island.

Located just thirteen degrees above the equator, where a projectile needs less velocity to achieve orbit than from sites at more northern latitudes, it provided an eight-thousand-kilometer test range, stretching across the Caribbean Sea and the South Atlantic Ocean, to the coast of

Africa. It was also positioned to take advantage of a series of radar-tracking and receiving stations, used by the Americans to monitor rocket firings from Cape Canaveral, Florida.

The next six months were busy ones for Bull. Site organization and facility construction in Barbados and at Highwater required extensive travel, and he threw himself into the effort. "Glorious days...I ran myself ragged all over North America," is how he would later describe it.

In order to minimize the separation from his family, Gerry often brought them to the pleasant climes of Barbados when his work there required extensive stays. Mimi recalls that they "would rent a house for three or four weeks...prices were very reasonable then." And, since their four young sons had not yet started school, the whole clan could spend more time together. Later, as the children entered classes in Montréal, these periods would grow less frequent, but the family spent at least a month each year together in Barbados, during the entire run of the HARP project.

While the five-inch tests at Aberdeen had proven the initial concept, the HARP project would also work with seven- and sixteen-inch guns. In their final development phase, these launchers would share the following characteristics. First, they were all constructed out of scrap naval and army gun barrels and mountings. Secondly, all the barrels were smooth-bored and, almost without exception, used saboted, smaller-than-tube-diameter projectiles. Thirdly, to produce higher muzzle velocities, their final forms consisted of joined barrel sections, which were kept straight with the aid of external cladding, and threaded bracing rods or tightened steel wires.

In the fall of 1961, Bull visited Aberdeen and, along with Charlie Murphy, arranged for the first transfer of what would become the most spectacular of his launchers. The U.S. Navy supplied the first surplus, 140-ton, 16-inch battleship gun, through an Office of Naval Research (ONR) contract with the University of Toronto. They paid for the smooth-boring of this 1920s-era weapon at the Watervliet Arsenal in New York State.

In a world that is used to the phrase, *multi-billion*, attached to anything involved with space research, the sizes of the contracts involved in HARP are laughable. In January of 1962, when the BRL arranged a contract for McGill to be provided with gun barrels, obsolete powder charges from World War II, and other surplus equipment, the price, exclusive of shipping, was $2,000!

By April 1962, McGill had initiated site preparation in Barbados. The next month, Bull enlisted the support of the U.S. army to transport the barrels and mounts to the island. The first two Mark 1 guns, bored out to 16.4 inches, were loaded aboard a U.S. army transport vessel, the huge, amphibious landing-ship, *John D. Page.*

Prevented by low cliffs and a coral reef from beaching directly in front of the gun site, the *Page* put the 140-ton barrel sections ashore several miles up the coast, by means of a specially laid railway track that ran directly inland from the ship's main deck. Once the barrels and their flat-bed railway cars were winched over the beach to the flatlands beyond, the track behind them was taken up, and the sections laid ahead of the cars. This was repeated until the barrels reached the mounting site, between the east end of the Seawell International Airport and the ocean. Here, a concrete revetment had been constructed, with an old coastal-defense gun-mount set at a forty-five-degree angle, to allow the first barrel to be elevated almost vertically.

Geza Kardos, who received his M.Sc. degree from McGill in 1957, was the local manager for HARP from August until the successful completion of the first firings, in January of 1963. He spent long, hard months directing the local workers in the installation of the gun, in its forty-foot-deep concrete emplacement. The work went on day and night, in sun and driving rain, with scientists and laborers alike hauling on ropes and winch handles. Stating he was "completely worn out" at the successful completion of the job, Kardos gratefully returned to McGill and more scholarly pursuits.

While the Foul Bay site offered many advantages to HARP, its remoteness from the North American supply and engineering centers, in Montréal and Aberdeen, required that powder magazines, maintenance shops and projectile-assembly buildings be provided. To house the administrative offices and the launch control center, an old plantation mansion on the site was reconstructed. Known as Paragon House, its treed grounds and stone fences provided a charming, nineteenth-century environment for Bull and his staff, as well as being a temporary bunkhouse for visitors and employees.

Prime Minister Barrow's firm support of HARP grew largely from Bull's policy of hiring local people to work on the program, in positions that were far from menial. At its height, HARP would employ over three hundred local workers and technicians. As Barbados approached full independence, his encouragement of young, black students to follow careers in science and technology, was widely noted and approved.

In later years, Bull would be accused, by segments of the North American media, of being a virulent racist and ultra-right-winger, for selling arms to South Africa. While not necessarily agreeing with the arms transfers, none of the islanders who worked with him over fifteen years share that view. Island resident Carlton Braithwaite, who was later to be an executive with Bull's Space Research Corporation, said, "Gerald Bull was one of the most color-blind men I ever met...he did not generalize about people...he cared only about what you thought or did, irrespective of color."

Braithwaite, as Assistant Manager for the Barbados HARP site, was a dynamic presence on the project. Twenty-eight years of age in 1963, he was the buffer between McGill personnel and the local people and their customs. His tasks included negotiations with the local labor force, merchants and government officials. Many would later state that, at the Paragon House headquarters, "Ask Carlton," was the phrase most often heard.

A mile to the northwest of the gun site, on the far side of the Seawell airport runways, a cluster of Aberdeen-modified tracking radars was established, their dishes staring perpetually toward the zenith. Camera-tracking stations were set up, both near the gun site and at remote locations up to three hundred kilometers away on other Caribbean islands, such as St. Vincent, Grenada, Tobago and Trinidad, to visually track the firings. A network of radio-based data and voice communications stations linked the sites.

While five- and seven-inch launch tubes were also set up on the site, it was the firing of the mighty sixteen-inch gun for the first time, in January of 1962, that dramatised Project HARP. Adorned with the crests of McGill, Aberdeen's BRL and The U.S. Army's Research Office, which Mimi Bull had carefully painted on the barrel, the gleaming white tube was elevated skyward and the launch area cleared for hundreds of yards around. In the control bunker, reinforced with sandbags and heavy timbers, Gerry Bull watched nervously as retired Canadian Army Colonel Roy Croft, the range safety officer, flipped a final switch. With a roar that could be heard for miles around, the HARP gun fired, and a dramatic mushroom cloud of smoke and fire issued from its muzzle. A large crowd of fascinated Barbadians, watching from the nearby bluffs, joined the cheers of the HARP crew at the success of the inaugural shot.

Basic as the gun-launched concept was, converting the guns to their new role was not as simple as it might seem. Conventional ballistic tables, based on the firing of ton-and-a-half rifled military shells at relatively low velocities, were found to have little relevance to the in-barrel behavior of lightweight, high-velocity projectiles and the explosive charges propelling them. The problems were compounded by the cost necessity of using old granular and stick-propellant charges, with inconveniently variable burn rates. As Bull would later say, "The initial muzzle velocities were very disappointing...the test [slugs] weren't going nearly fast enough."

A combination of new theoretical studies and practical firings soon produced answers. With heavy military shells, the high pressures in the breech were maintained down the barrel by the projectile's mass-resisting acceleration. The lightweight shells moved out quicker. This meant the breech pressures dropped off while the barrel pressures rose, wasting much of the propulsive energy and threatening to burst the tubes. While the later use of modern propellant charges, with stable burn rates, aided the process, the basic solution turned out to be separating the charge into several bundles spaced out with plywood dividers, and firing them simultaneously. In Bull's words, "We tailored the gun to burn just like a rocket...we had to calculate the pressure at every place in that darn gun...but it worked out eventually." After the break-in period, HARP guns began to achieve muzzle velocities of up to seven thousand feet per second.

Barbados was only the "sharp end" of the HARP project. Back in Montréal, at Highwater and Aberdeen, the new projectiles and the research loads for them were conceived and produced. Dr.Leslie Jaeger, a professor of civil engineering at McGill, was responsible for the structural design and integrity of the 470-pound shells for the big 16-inch, work he delivered on time and to specifications. He also served as the project's engineering director in Barbados for the initial phases. For the five- and seven-inch guns, Charlie Murphy and his team at BRL designed a series of sleek, dart-like carriers for a variety of tiny instrument packages and chemical payloads. In common with most of the sixteen-inch projectiles, they were sabot rounds, and used a drop-away "pusher plate" of aluminum, steel or plastic at their bases. By November 1962, payloads from these systems were reaching altitudes of 215,000 feet. Problems with the transmission range of the little onboard transmitters aside, the shots proved that electronics could stand up to the high accelerations and still produce useful information.

Yet, if the smaller-diameter guns and projectiles were to explore the lower atmospheric envelope, the big sixteen-inchers were designed to reach the edge of space and beyond.

Still driven by the memory of Sputnik, the North American scientific community was still under political and popular pressure to "get going on space and overtake the Soviets." to quote a newspaper editorial of the time. Understanding "the doorway to space," the atmosphere in the rarefied heights beyond the reach of balloons and winged aircraft, became a critical need. HARP was to do more than any other single project in the world to meet the demand for basic information on which scientists could work.

While rocket probes could easily reach sub-space altitudes, they could not long remain in the regions they sought to explore, because of their high speeds and the pull of gravity. For point measurements, this could be accepted, but for observation durations of even several hours, many launches were required, and rockets were expensive. HARP could do nothing about the duration of individual probes in the boundaries of space, but the project got around the quandary by providing a cheap launch system that radically reduced the costs per shot.

Named after the mythical bird on the McGill crest, the first Martlet series of projectiles was designed by Bull and his associates, based on the old CARDE range experiences. The Montréal firm of Aviation Electric produced the basic projectile, while Computing Devices of Canada (CDC) installed the telemetry transmitters in their Ottawa facilities, and sent specialists Ross Freeman and Laurie Phillips to Barbados to set up the telemetry receivers.

Other specific sensor packages were installed in the McGill laboratories, or on site. While the Martlets could, and did, loft a wide variety of probes into near space, the most important was a simple chemical release experiment.

One humorous soul has described the often-photographed Martlet 1A as looking like a model rocket made for a grade-school play, and the analogy is not too far off. It was simply a system test bed that did not try to be fancy or particularly aerodynamic. Years later, Bull would sketch the basic Martlet program as follows. "Martlet 2A was the first high-altitude projectile. It weighed 225 pounds. The forebody carried electronics, the aftbody carried chemical payloads. It was five inches in diameter, and it had a very heavy pusher plate. The actual, all-up weight was around 400 to 450 pounds. Then what happened was the Martlet 2C. [It] was the big workhorse, still a five-inch. Then, towards the end, we came up with a 350-pound vehicle, the same thing, only seven inches in diameter.

"The idea was to find out what happens in the atmosphere from sunset to sunrise. Remember, nobody gave us grants. We had to produce topical atmospheric meteorological for the [U.S.] army research office, that's how we got our money. We were trying to measure everything to the top of the atmosphere, which we labeled as a nominal two hundred kilometers. What we were trying to measure was the motion of the layers from seventy-five to two hundred kilometers, and also lower levels, measuring beyond normal meteorological instrumentation."

Bull stressed the low cost of the system, compared to the cheapest sounding rockets at around $75,000 apiece, exclusive of support costs. "The cost of a launch was about $5,000. We did up to eight a night. We used to do three nights in a row to try and get the data."

He also explained the low-tech approach of measuring ultra-high-altitude winds. "What we had at the end of the projectile was a chemical release...it left a trail. Imagine you have a cigarette in your hand, and the smoke will just rise in a straight line and then it breaks into turbulence. If there's a wind, it will start to move with the wind. If you can measure that movement...in other words, you take photographs at very short intervals and identify the points, then you get the motion. That's the basic idea.

"All of these programs were intimately associated with National Atmospheric Program in North America. [Dr. N.W.] Rosenberg, at the United States Air Force Cambridge Research Laboratory, pioneered this technique, and suggested that, if we could put it into the gun, it would be ideal."

It was, although the chemicals involved were extremely dangerous, and had to be loaded into the projectile at the launch site in a special building, by men in fire suits. If any spilled and caught fire, it could only be put out in a very odd way.

As Gerry Bull explained it, "We put about five to seven pounds of this stuff, liquid trimethyl aluminum, eighty percent, and twenty percent triethyl aluminum, in the projectiles. This mixture burns with air at contact, at tremendous temperature. But, strangely, you put it out by pouring gasoline on it. Maybe that's why everybody thought we were all nuts. You see, the flame is so hot, there is no other way to smother it...if you put gasoline on it, then you have a gasoline fire, which you could extinguish. Strange, eh?"

Release of radar-trackable chaff clouds and small aluminized balloons, at altitudes up to 150 kilometers, was also part of the experiments. Measurement of magnetic-field strengths was another endeavor. Even the re-entry of the projectiles yielded valuable data. In the relative vacuum of the high atmosphere, the projectiles fell back into the atmosphere at the same attitude they left it (nose up, tail down). The radar "flutter," as they nosed back over in the thickening air, told much about conditions in the "tumble zone," sixty kilometers high.

By the end of the atmospherics program, close to a thousand shots would be fired. To this day, nearly half the world's data base on upper atmospheric conditions remains HARP-derived.

Yet the Barbados gun firings were not the only things on Bull's agenda. The development of the Highwater site continued apace. Much of what had been naked wood in the early days, now took on a more settled aspect. Structures like the new fire-control center were now neat, white-painted clapboard bunglalows, and the administration building was a pleasant, stone structure beside a small lake.

At the gun sites, however, the raw look still showed, in torn earth marred by construction litter and bulldozer tracks.

Expanding on the CARDE range concept, a second smooth-bore-barrel sixteen-inch was set up for Martlet projectile tests. This barrel was the first extended-tube system designed to increase muzzle velocity. The breech section was cut off a second sixteen-incher, and the remaining tube was attached to the first gun, changing it from an L45 to an L83 piece.

In the gunner's lexicon, the *L* in the above figures stands for length. To grasp what 45 and 83 refer to, it helps to understand the artillery world's confusing use of the word *caliber*. The first, and most generally understood, use refers to the interior barrel diameter, as in sixteen-inch caliber. The second use is *barrel caliber*. This defines the tube's length in multiples of its interior diameter. Thus, L83 means the

Highwater HARP barrel was 110.66 feet long. When this later had a further extension added, its barrel caliber became L126, or 168 feet.

With elevation limited to a maximum of ten degrees, payload shells at Highwater were fired up to four kilometers into earthen butts, where they could be recovered and studied, as well as photographed in flight with telemetry signals recorded.

Not all the shells worked. Some collapsed in the barrel under accelerations of up to ten thousand gravities, while others suffered from electronic failures. The most spectacular incidents were failures of the sabots to separate cleanly, causing the projectile to tumble at multi-sonic velocities—"hell of a noise," is how one witness described it. In one celebrated case, a shell broke up and spread its load of chemical fire over several kilometers of forest.

As Charlie Murphy would point out, this was considered a normal part of the development process. Failure led the way to modifications, and they, in turn, produced successful firings.

Though it was minor, compared to the HARP project, Bull and the McGill space team concurrently conducted other high-speed research for corporations and government agencies in both Canada and the United States.

NASA, the American space agency, was one of those organizations. In June of 1962, they awarded Bull and McGill's mechanical engineering department a contract to study the impact of micrometeorites on the hulls of space capsules. Charlie Murphy and another scientist, William Friend, who was slated to have a long association with Bull, worked under his direction on the project.

At that time, many of the effects of low-mass, hyper-velocity collisions were puzzling and not much understood. At CARDE, Bull had developed a gun that used oxygen and hydrogen instead of conventional explosives. Moved to the Highwater site, it was connected to a vacuum tank in which material samples were bombarded with tiny "bullets," at speeds up to fifty thousand miles per hour. The results of these tests were a significant aid to understanding hyper-velocity phenomena, and contributed much to early American spacecraft design.

While General Trudeau left the army in 1962, the R & D branch continued to enthusiastically support Bull's work under Major General Chester Clarke, the new Chief of Army Research. Trudeau himself followed the path of many senior retired U.S. military officers, by accepting an executive position with American industry. In 1962, he became head of Gulf Oil's Research and Development company, a position he held until his retirement in July of 1968. Even though he had left the service, his friendship with Bull continued, and he was a frequent visitor to the Barbados and Highwater sites.

As Bull pointed out earlier, producing atmospheric research data was HARP's major source of funding at this time. Yet his ideas for the further use of HARP concepts for space research required more money. Much as he may have detested it, he was forced to go knocking on the Canadian government's door.

CHAPTER 7

While Project HARP ran into the mid-sixties, Gerry Bull's existence was still a hectic round of travel and work, even though his lifestyle had long lost any traces of its former austerity. Besides the house in St. Bruno, the Bulls now had a second home at Highwater. In 1963, Gerry and Mimi had a large, elegant, A-frame house custom-built on a three-hundred-acre parcel of land, which was held separate from the rest of the test site. It became the center of a complex that grew to include tennis courts, a swimming pool and guest houses. Since Bull was spending more time at Highwater to oversee projectile tests, the new home, just minutes away from the gun butts, added to the time Gerry could spend with his family.

Other changes would, unfortunately, subtract from those hours. The Bulls now had six children, their last son, Robert, having been born in August 1964, and their first daughter, Kathleen, in June of 1965. With two babies to attend to, and the older boys in grade school, Mimi had to spend more of her time in St. Bruno, and less of it than she would have liked at Highwater and Barbados. "At that time, it was mostly the summers when I was able to get away," Mimi recalled.

While they did not have a permanent residence in Barbados, their frequent visits made Gerry and Mimi part of a new and multi-racial social circle emerging on the island. It was an eclectic mix of local educators, prominent businessmen, and old colonial officers. It also included rising black political figures such as Prime Minister Eric Barrow, who quickly became a friend of the Bulls. This new-found social environment built up a base of influence and support that was to greatly benefit Bull in the years ahead.

Considering the changes of fortune the HARP project was to endure, the period, in retrospect, was destined to be one of missed opportunities. Yet, it also has to be remembered that, for many of the people who worked on it—the HARPies, as some still call themselves—those years were great times, and fun ones, as well.

For those who were in Barbados for any length of time, especially the younger men who had never left Canada before, the hot sun, strange smells and brilliant colors of the island added a touch of exotic excitement to their work. Besides the joys of fishing, swimming and exploring, the pressures of their labors produced some remarkable blowouts. Paragon House saw some wild parties of almost Animal-House proportions. But, so involved were the HARPies in their work, the affairs never ended in bacchanals that would keep them from the range in the morning. Indeed, to the chagrin of the few women who dared to attend, the evenings often ended as raucous debates over their work. "An incredible mixture of strong rum and science," is how one participant, who prefers to remain anonymous, describes them. While these affairs tended to happen only while "the boss" was safely out the country, they are another reminder of the energy and sense of enjoyment that Bull's leadership engendered throughout the project.

For all the cheer Gerry Bull showed to his co-workers, his relationship with the Canadian government gave him no cause to smile as the decade progressed. He was to write, years later, in *Paris Guns and Project HARP*, that. "The Canadian government, for reasons antedating and non related to any technical aspects, did not support the (HARP) programme at its inception..."

What the quote means is that he felt there was a personal motivation, on the part of his enemies at DRB, National Defence Headquarters and Trade and Commerce, to deny funding to whatever he was working on.

Even though he was no longer directly connected with DRB, Bull took delight in the steady decline of its fortunes during the mid-sixties. He correctly saw them as a spent force. "They weren't doing anything new anymore," is how he put it.

The newly elected Liberal government of Lester Pearson stripped DRB of its responsibilities for Canadian space research in 1965. A new civilian Ministry of Communications took over Canada's Allouette I and II communications satellites, which were launched by American rockets. While many of DRB's components would outlive its demise at the end of the decade, it's role as "the fourth arm of Canada's defense," had vanished long before that.

Now retired, George Lindsey was for many years a senior scientist with the DRB. In 1964, he was four years into his twenty-year tenure as chief of its Operational Research Group, one of those DRB organizations that continues within the Canadian Armed Forces structure to this day. The position gave him a clear view of Bull's relations with the government funding apparatus, at the time of the HARP project.

"The group I was with was very much interested in ballistic missile defense, and space research generally. We reckoned that Canada would never be able to put satellites into orbit on its own, because the launch costs were so great...What Bull was promising to do was to put small satellites into orbit fired from a gun. We were really quite impressed about it. There were two schools of thought...a lot of people in this department thought it was a great idea...we in our group were rooting for it. But there were others who disliked him, and whether they disliked him for scientific or political reasons I never found out. They may have been mad at Gerry, they may not have wanted to take American contracts, or they may have thought that everything should be done by NASA."

Lindsay stated a common view at DRB, when he said, "I think he was a bit paranoid. Anytime some unfortunate thing happened to him, he probably thought there was a whole great army out to get him. I don't think it was quite as sinister as that."

It is easy to sympathize with Bull's frustration, if not his conclusions. He was running a space program on amounts of money that NASA would have kept in a piggy bank. While it is difficult to give a dollar value to his scrounging of parts and logistics support, the fact that actual McGill financial support in the first few years never exceeded $250,000, gives one an idea of the scale of the operation.

Another problem was the nature of his American army support, and the limitations placed on it by their government. In 1964, as it does today, U.S. law actually forbade their army to participate in space research, or to develop launchers with a range greater than sixty miles. Considering that armies, not air forces, began ballistic-missile development, it was a strange state of affairs. German rocket research in World War II was carried out by their ground forces. Ballistic missiles, such as the V-2, were seen as a form of extended range artillery, and so naturally became an army weapon.

The Americans continued this approach at the end of the European war. When German rocket scientists, such as Werner Von Braun, were brought to the United States, the rocket programs they were employed on were army ones. The first American launch of a satellite was carried out by a modified army Redstone rocket.

The Soviets and the space race were to change all that. After the shock of the Sputnik launch, the American government found itself with a scattered space effort. Besides the army rockets, the navy had its Vanguard program, and the air force yet another set of objectives. The necessity for a unified effort to beat the Soviets in space was obvious. With the creation of NASA and the civilian-oriented goal of sending a man to the moon, most of the army space program, precisely because it was the biggest and most developed, was transferred to it. Von Braun, along with the rest of the German rocketeers, became a NASA employee.

That left the military space aspect, and here, inter-service rivalries came to the fore. The air force's argument was two-fold. First, if it had a man on board, it was a flying machine and that could only be an air force job. Secondly, since intermediate and intercontinental-range ballistic missiles with nuclear warheads were a strategic weapon that duplicated the air force's B-52 strategic bomber fleet, both should be under a common command and control system.

The U.S. navy was able to keep its capabilities by coming up with the concept of submarine-launched ballistic systems, such as Polaris and Trident. Thus, the triad concept of air force bombers and ICBMs, balanced by seaborne naval missiles was born. While the U.S. army protested, it lost both in Congress and at the Joint Chiefs of Staff level. With the formation of NASA, it was stripped of all its previous responsibilities. HARP, as a gun-based system for meteorological work, was able to circumvent this.

Yet the real purpose of HARP, as Bull, Murphy and Mordell saw it, was to ultimately launch satellites; something the U.S. army could no longer fund. But, with its promise of low costs, HARP was an attractive and exciting proposition. As George Lindsay pointed out, many scientists liked the idea, and Bull got increasing support in his lobbying efforts with the Canadian government.

In response to the rising clamor from Dean Mordell and many of their own staffers, the Canadian government, in mid-1964, grudgingly reversed its position on HARP funding. Agreeing to match U.S. money, to the tune of $2,500,000 per annum for a minimum of three years, it entered into a jointly funded program with the U.S. army and McGill. It's purpose was to demonstrate a gun-launched orbital system for the Ministry of Defence Production. To handle the project and simplify administration, McGill's engineering department created the Space Research Institute, and Dr. Gerald Bull became its director.

Grudging was the operative word, and the agreement, which was something less than a legally binding document, broke down from the word *go*. Money that was committed for the period between June 1964

and May of 1965 was not paid to McGill until the very last month. Only Mordell's use of McGill funds to cover the shortfall allowed the work to begin. Worse, Bull discovered that the three-year commitment wasn't worth the paper it was written on. As press articles of the time attest, there was always speculation about the "controversial project," and endless Defence Production reviews of their participation in what some clever souls took to calling "Bull's pipe dream."

Bull had been spoiled by several years of U.S. funding. While it was limited in scope and amount, it was given in an unstinting manner, and with an understanding of the problems that accompany any technical development. With the HARP orbiter project, he was once again reminded of the dominant role of politicians in Canadian program funding.

Even more than their Conservative predecessors, whom he had encountered in his CARDE days, the new Liberal MPs and cabinet ministers lacked any real appreciation of what was involved in HARP. They cared more about where the money was being spent than on what, and there were no Canadian voters in Barbados. Nor was there a Liberal Member of Parliament in the riding where Highwater was located. It had a stubborn tradition of being one of the few areas in the province of Quebec that routinely elected Conservatives, at the time. The machine politics of the Québec wing of the Liberal party did not look kindly on spending government money in a place like that.

To be fair, however, there were also scientists and engineers who honestly didn't believe in the project's utility or technical feasibility. What Bull called the "conventional electronics people" doubted that the suggested orbital payloads could stand the tremendous acceleration when traveling down the barrels or, even if they could, that they would be of a useful size when they arrived in space.

Nevertheless, Bull did have more money, and near the end of 1964, work commenced on converting the Barbados sixteen-inch gun to a longer tube. A ten-caliber extension was welded and bracketed to the standard L45-caliber barrel. While this expedient failed on the eleventh test shot, it proved the utility of the barrel-extension concept.

Following this, work started on the most dramatic-looking (and certainly the most photographed) of the HARP guns, the L86. As with the Highwater guns, another barrel, minus the breech section, was to be added to the original. The extension was smooth-bored in an old U.S. Navy gun factory at Pocatello, Idaho, and delivered to the Barbados site. Extensive rebuilding and deepening of the gun pit was required. New recoil cylinders and hydraulic mechanisms had to be installed. Production and welding of the stiffening "rib cage" and the torsion bar assemblies directly onto the barrel was contracted to Davie Shipbuilding of Québec (Now MIL Davie).

Emile Robinson remembers the time well. Now retired as a ship builder, from MIL Davie's Lauzom, Québec, yard, he and fellow-workers Rodger Dumont and Gerald Robert worked on the HARP guns both at Highwater and Barbados. From their scrapbooks and memories, they detailed what Robinson described as "the most exciting job I ever worked on."

"Bull, now he was quite a man," Dumont recalls. "At first, some of the scientists, the young men, eh?, they would not talk to us directly about the job...Bull would come down and ignore the foreman. He came directly to us and asked how it was going. If you had a suggestion, he would say, 'You know best; you do it.'"

As with just about anyone who ever worked for Bull, Robinson stressed his ability to generate enthusiasm and get things done in a cooperative atmosphere. "He made everybody feel they were doing something special...something important." He also recalls Gerry Bull's cavalier approach to economics and established procedures. "He would come down to the yard, look at something, and order changes on the spot. When the company would ask who was going to pay for it, Bull would say, 'Don't worry, send us the bill...We'll figure it out somehow.' He always did find a way...he was quite the juggler."

As a skilled welding technician, Robinson spent a year working on Project HARP in places as diverse as Highwater, Barbados and Yuma, Arizona, where a second L86 gun was set up, purely for the purposes of meteorological work.

The great weight of the compound guns made on-site metalwork essential. George Bronson, Chief of Manufacturing at the Highwater Laboratory, designed and built a portable boring and honing device that could travel down the tube to give it its final finish. To overcome the erosion of the barrel, a special half-inch-thick liner of high-grade steel, which could be replaced after approximately fifty firings, was inserted in the tube.

In March, 1965, the L86 was fired for the first time, and the test was a complete success. The first step, in what Gerry Bull saw as Canada's march into space, was complete.

The L86 was capable of giving the lightweight Martlet 2-series projectile a muzzle velocity of seven thousand feet per second; conversely, it could fire a much heavier load at around five thousand feet per second. Yet, impressive at the velocity was, and despite the fact that it could lob packages into space, it was still far too slow to make them stay there (Orbital velocity is twenty-five thousand feet per second).

Gerry Bull explained how he was going to get there. "The ideal solution was to mate the rocket to the gun. It's very, very easy. It just takes new computers; high-school kids could do it. Start a rocket from the earth's surface at five thousand feet a second, and it's an amazing improvement in performance."

Indeed. With the hybrid gun-rocket system, the tube took the place of the huge first stage of a conventional rocket, allowing the relatively small and inexpensive upper stages to begin their burn in the ultra-thin air of the upper atmosphere, where their thrust was maximized.

As early as 1963, Highwater began testing sub-caliber rocket rounds, to see how they withstood the tremendous acceleration of gun-launching. This led to the Martlet 3A sub-caliber, gun-fired rocket. Its original objective was to lob a forty-pound payload to over three hundred miles. Preliminary firings at the Barbados and Highwater sites (which did not include rocket ignition, and were conducted before Canadian government funding became available) showed serious engineering problems.

Hit with up to six thousand gravities, the propellant grains in the projectiles tended to break up and extrude through the nozzles. Since modern rockets use a hollow, star-shaped core up their centers to achieve high-efficiency burning, it was a serious problem. The answer was found by filling the core with a zinc bromide liquid solution, equal in density to the rocket propellant that could be drained out of the projectile after it had left the gun barrel.

The effect was to make the entire mass act as a solid. As Bull described it, "At Highwater, we took an old gun and fired very long, solid rockets out of it. See, my argument is simple. If you imagine that the rocket is nothing more than a solid piece of rubber, you put it in nice and tight, and you push at one end, it squeezes back and pushes the wall of the tube, no? It works like an elastic-type spring that can withstand the shock."

A number of Canadian and American firms took part in developing Martlet 3, and later Martlet 4, rocket systems because they clearly saw the inherent possibilities. Besides Canadian Industries Ltd., California-based concerns like Lockheed Propulsion, Rocketdyne and Aerojet General developed and manufactured fuels, casings and nozzle arrangements. Their interest in, and support of, HARP was so great that their contributions were to greatly exceed any financial remuneration. Few outside of HARP, and certainly none in the Canadian government, ever appreciated what a deal this was in reducing overall program costs.

Another bugaboo was to bedevil HARP. In any scientific or engineering development program, there are two types of problems—those that are fixable and those that are not. The first type always occurs; indeed, discovering and overcoming them is what the development process is all about. The second type is rarer, but more profound—it means the basic idea is screwed, and the concept will never work.

For those outside the world of science, the difference is seldom appreciated. The visitor to a test that fails is not impressed by the promise that it will work eventually. The fact that scientists, being

human, tend to claim that all problems are Type One until repeated failure proves otherwise, does not help the process.

HARP certainly had its failures—projectile structural collapses, improper sabot separation, electronics failing at random marred many of the preliminary shots. In July of 1964, ten out of twenty-three Martlet 2 firings either failed or did not reach expected altitudes. This last defect was mostly the result of using ancient powder charges, and the incomplete understanding of how to maintain optimum breech/ barrel pressures, as previously discussed. To politicians and bureaucrats, the effect was to make HARP look chancy; hence the repeated press use of the word *controversial*, in describing the project. No matter how much Dean Mordell and Bull would explain that these were normal and expected difficulties, the message didn't really get through.

That Bull's original lobbying approach had stressed the simplicity and "no-hassles" benefits of the program didn't help either. His single-minded obsession with his work was also a problem. Whether naïveté can be claimed as an excuse, or should be viewed as a failure in outlook, is a moot point, but Gerry Bull certainly suffered from it. His belief that science should be judged on its worth was, as he would later admit, "very naïve."

Even his considerable understanding of how the process of funding acquisition really worked, did not move him to be more effective at it. The best that can be said is that he was great, in a tactical sense, but poor on strategic outlooks. His idealism tended to ignore what his intellect knew. When his frustrations finally drove him to act, he often left an impression of petulance.

A scientist who observed some of the inter-governmental meetings over HARP funding said, "He was too kind, in a way...his approach was to say, 'Look, I know money's short, so I've come up with a way to do it cheaper...this is the bottom line on what I need.' He made a conscious effort to cut things to the bone."

Bull should have known that, in the perceived interests of economy, the government seldom gave research projects all they asked for. "Cut to the bone" estimates can't tolerate cost overruns, and HARP was fated to have them.

"It was a great idea," the NRC scientist recalls. "It got a lot of people excited in spite of themselves. 'Canada in space? Sure, why not?' If it had successfully evolved, we [presumably NRC] were prepared to support it to the hilt...the platform possibilities were endless.

"It's hindsight now...but Gerry asked for $10,000,000, firm, over three fiscal years...I think he should have asked for more, a lot more...he would have got at least some of it."

Reality was a Catch-22 situation that devolved into a vicious circle. Development was supposed to proceed concurrently in a number of related fields, but short funding and payment delays tripped up the schedules. Thus, development lagged, objectives weren't met, and the Ministry of Defence Production, under Bud Drury, who detested Bull personally for the baboon remark, got nervous about the project's feasibility. The response was to question whether they should complete their obligation to HARP, and funding was held up while they debated the issue.

Yet, in spite of the bureaucratic haggling, Bull and Murphy got a lot of work going in the initial stages. The next step in the Martlet 3 series was the E model, which was a full-bore, seven-inch projectile with a fiberglass-wrapped rocket motor and flipout stabilization fins at the rear. Fired from the BRL seven-inch, smooth-bore gun, at a muzzle velocity of 4,000 feet per second, it lobbed 44-pound payloads to altitudes of over 155 miles.

As of July 1964, when Canada agreed to contribute funding, the official goal of HARP was to orbit a satellite. The Martlet 4 series was the designated launch vehicle. Designed to be fired from the L83 sixteen-inch Barbados gun, it was a full-bore, (16.6 inch diameter) three-stage rocket, capable of delivering a 50-pound payload to a 265-mile-high circular orbit. Pencil thin, Martlet 4 weighed less than a ton, and stood just twenty-nine feet high.

Since it was designed to reach orbit, the new spacecraft had to deal with a problem the earlier Martlets didn't face—attitude control in the vacuum of space. It was here that Bull's enemies, "the conventional electronics people," or whatever one wishes to call them, had their largest doubts about the system's workability.

A fin-stabilized rocket, burning in the lower atmosphere, has little problem in maintaining its heading. But, after gun launch, the Martlet 4's first-stage rocket burnt out at an altitude of twenty-five miles, far above the height where aerodynamic controls can work. The attitude stability of remaining stages was to be maintained by spinning them with small thrusters. To do that, a system to sense and remember the projectiles heading was required.

In rockets and space capsules of 1960s design, the guidance package consisted of a series of tiny attitude-control jets, controlled by a gimbaled arrangement of gyroscopes and acceleration-measuring devices. Especially in the case of war rockets, it had the advantage of being self-contained and unjammable. Perfecting this mechanical arrangement to work for missiles and space probes, which were subjected to stresses up to twenty times the force of gravity, was hard enough. No one, including Gerry Bull, expected these delicate devices to withstand five thousand Gs in the gun barrel. Another way had to be found.

A combined electronics team from McGill, BRL and the Harry Diamond Laboratory, with Aviation Electric Limited of Montréal as prime contractor, came up with an innovative answer that did not involve gyroscopes. Backed up by a radio link to a ground-based computer, Martlet 4 used a system of infra-red sun and horizon sensors to determine its position in space. Because they were solid-state devices, the guidance packages could stand gun launches and still guide the Martlet into a 265-mile-high circular orbit.

At least, it should have. The above descriptions are couched in "as if" terms, but Martlet 4 was not to be. A system that would have orbited Canadian satellites at costs per pound, delivered to orbit, as low as five percent of a conventional rocket launch, never made it past a collection of tested parts and the dreams of its designer.

By the middle of 1965, it became apparent to Bull and his co-workers that program progress, hamstrung as it was by research and funding delays, plus the constant threat of instant cancellation, would not result in a successful launch by the end of the three-year period agreed to with the Ministry of Defence Production.

But 1967, the target date for the HARP satellite, was also the hundredth anniversary of Canada. For the centennial, several hundred million dollars would be spent on parties, commemorative events and historical projects. While many of these served useful purposes, most of them just resulted in long speeches about how wonderful Canada was. Wilfred Laurier's famous—and now obviously incorrect—statement that "the twentieth century belongs to Canada," was repeated *ad nauseam*.

Meanwhile, back at Highwater, Gerry Bull hadn't given up on his private objective, a spectacular contribution to the national birthday party. Balked in his attempts to see Martlet 4 orbit in the project timeframe, he came up with another, cheaper alternative, as a symbolic gesture, a last, desperate attempt to orbit the Canadian flag.

To understand one of the reasons it didn't happen, it helps to compare this Canadian space program with NASA and its biggest creation, the 160-meter-high Vertical Assembly Building at Cape Canaveral, Florida. Built in the 1960s, to stack the Saturn moon rockets, it is in the Guiness Book of World Records as the largest uninterrupted volume ever enclosed by a single structure. At 3.6 million cubic meters, it is so huge that, without an air-conditioning system, rainfall would occur inside it. Now used to mate the components of the two thousand-ton space shuttle, it is a monument to something Charlie Murphy says should always be spelled with capital letters—BIG SCIENCE.

Contrast that gigantic structure with another image. In Bull's book, *Paris Guns and Project Harp*, there is a picture of a Martlet 2G-1 projectile entering the Highwater assembly shop for mating with its sabot sections. No massive, fifteen thousand-ton, tracked-vehicle transporters, no hordes of masked and white-jacketed technicians in ultra-sterile "clean rooms". Instead, an unpainted, rough-lumber shed, and five guys in grubby overalls watching a light crane swing a sleek, fifteen-foot dart onto a trolley. Replace the Martlet with an engine block for a '55 Chevy, and the scene could be Joe's Garage in some backwater rural town.

Nothing so well illustrates that project HARP was "small science" as images like that. One can only wonder if the impression left with visiting bureaucrats and politicians was that something that looked this down-home couldn't really be serious. Perhaps Gerry Bull should have insisted on more dramatic-looking structures. Underground bunkers with armored doors might have been more impressive.

While it was "small science", Martlet 2G-1 was a brilliant example of cost-effective engineering and simplicity. As its series number implies, it was an upgrade of the original atmospheric-sounding probes. To bypass the developmental problems of the Martlet 4's full-bore rockets, the 2G-1's rocket stages were packaged in an 11.32-inch-diameter steel aeroshell, saboted up to 16.7 inches. It weighed less than 1,500 pounds.

It was the first, and perhaps the only, attempt in the world, to produce an *unguided* orbital vehicle. A high spin-up rate after launch, and precise timing, were the keys that allowed the final stages to naturally fall into the correct attitude for orbital insertion. True, the payload would not exceed 3.5 pounds, but the whole point of the HARP exercise was to prove the utility of gun-launched orbital systems, as a starter. But even this was not to be.

As Bull bitterly wrote, years later, in *Paris Guns and Project HARP*,

> Carried on as a covert part of the programme in a race against time, we had simply started the hardware building too late to beat the deadline of the group known generally as "The Torchers." This particular organization acts as the arm of those dedicated to destroying technical projects. Immediately that a policy decision can be achieved, it rushes into action to destroy (by torching and burning) all technical hardware, machinery, software, technical documentation, etc., to ensure that there is no chance of resurrection nor memorial to accomplishment.

This mention of "The Torchers" is a precise description of how the government of John Diefenbaker moved against the late, lamented Avro Arrow. Yet, the implication that the demise of HARP was the result of an ongoing, organized conspiracy within the government structure, irrespective of which party was in power, strains credulity. It imputes a clarity of purpose and intent for which there is no evidence.

To those who believe, without question, in their own star—and Gerry Bull was certainly one of those—simple, unbelievable stupidity can often be perceived as a result of a plot. But, the more one regards the matter, the easier it is to understand why Bull might have felt that way. "You call Bull paranoid," one man from the HARP days said, in a cold fury. "What he said might as bloody well have been true...the bureaucrats always win in this damn country!"

MARTLET 4

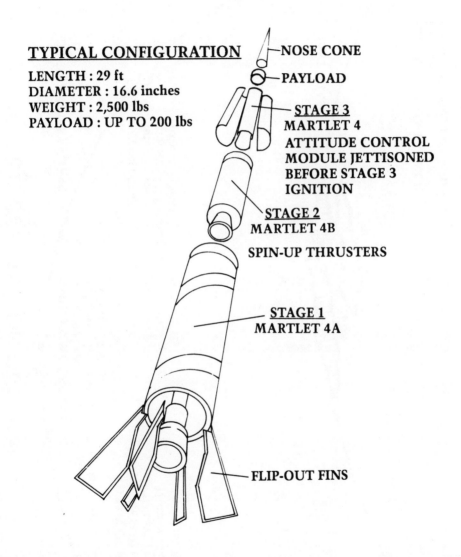

TYPICAL CONFIGURATION

LENGTH : 29 ft
DIAMETER : 16.6 inches
WEIGHT : 2,500 lbs
PAYLOAD : UP TO 200 lbs

NOSE CONE

PAYLOAD

STAGE 3
MARTLET 4
ATTITUDE CONTROL
MODULE JETTISONED
BEFORE STAGE 3
IGNITION

STAGE 2
MARTLET 4B

SPIN-UP THRUSTERS

STAGE 1
MARTLET 4A

FLIP-OUT FINS

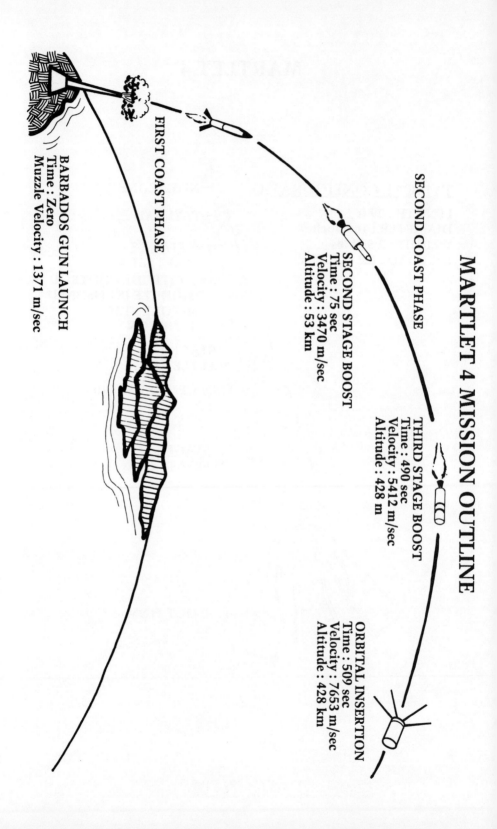

MARTLET 4 MISSION OUTLINE

BARBADOS GUN LAUNCH
Time : Zero
Muzzle Velocity : 1371 m/sec

FIRST COAST PHASE

SECOND STAGE BOOST
Time : 75 sec
Velocity : 3470 m/sec
Altitude : 53 km

SECOND COAST PHASE

THIRD STAGE BOOST
Time : 490 sec
Velocity : 5412 m/sec
Altitude : 428 m

ORBITAL INSERTION
Time : 509 sec
Velocity : 7653 m/sec
Altitude : 428 km

CHAPTER 8

"Paper kills" is an old bureaucratic adage that can be taken a number of ways. In the case of Project HARP, it translated as death by a thousand cuts. Early in 1966, newspaper articles and editorials, especially in the French-language daily, *La Presse*, began attacking the program. It asked what use the project served, in advancing the interests of a province then emerging from an almost-feudal past in the "quiet revolution" led by the provincial government of Liberal Jean Lesage. Bull would later claim that these attacks were orchestrated by his enemies in Ottawa, but the causes were wider than that

During the sixties, virtually every university campus in North America went through a period of protest and ferment, and McGill was no exception. Student demonstrations were one thing, but the reverberations from America's disastrous Vietnam war affected the outlooks of the faculty, as well. Where, a few short years before, military-related scientific programs were seen as useful, indeed valuable, adjuncts to the university's work, that was no longer so. As with the population at large, the old consensus, that defense work was morally and socially correct, shattered.

Due to the extensive financial support from American military sources, and claims that HARP was being considered as a possible launch platform for orbiting nuclear bombs, the program came under increasing criticism, from an ethical point of view. Student leaders flailed the engineering department as "the home of the Doctors of Death," and many of their teachers came to agree with them. Those in the faculty who had always been lukewarm to HARP, saying it tied up human and monetary resources that were better applied elsewhere, sat back and watched as its support base shrank.

Gerry Bull kept a surprisingly low profile during all of this. The newspaper accounts of the period are devoid of his comments, except for a few terse descriptions of the technical utility of HARP. Wisely, considering that the loathing toward him in the federal government was rising to new heights, he allowed his supporters to lead the defense.

Dean Donald Mordell fought hard for HARP, defending it at every turn. Not only did he lobby behind the scenes, he wrote letters to the editors of major newspapers across the country and gave numerous press interviews. In impeccable French, he bombarded *La Presse* with seldom-printed missives, outlining the social, economic and technical benefits to what he called, "our province." In a Montréal *Gazette* article of March 3, entitled "HARP Project—Lack of Ottawa Funds Hits Aim," he pointed out the disastrous effects that federal government indecision was having on their efforts. "We are not issuing any more new contracts," he said. "We are not making any new projectiles. We are at a standstill. If our funds are cut off we may have to release some of our staff, but we are reluctant to do this while the possibility remains that the government will back us."

Those who saw HARP's promise and understood its thrust came from a wide variety of backgrounds. David Orlikow, the New Democratic Party member for Winnipeg North, rose in the House of Commons on March 18. After calling HARP "one of the most exciting, one of the most imaginative scientific research programs ever developed in Canada," he warned that government inaction would lead to an American takeover of the work. He charged that senior officials at the Defence Research Board were actively "hostile" to Project HARP, and were out to destroy it. "They have made attempts," he said, "to have the project director dismissed."

He went on to say that, "The top officials...are antagonistic to any scientific project which has any relationship to defense, unless they can control it lock, stock and barrel." He said they were opposed to such work being controlled "by the actual people in the universities."

"Will U.S. Get McGill Space Plan?" a *Globe and Mail* headline of March 11, 1966, asked. The fear that the United States would acquire a valuable Canadian asset for next to nothing drove much of the opposition to the government's position, and it caused the Liberals to waffle, prolonging the suspense.

While Ottawa remained silent, the Space Research Institute was forced to lay off fifteen draftsmen, engineers and technicians, at the beginning of April. The dismissals affected work at both Highwater and Montréal.

Asked by the press if there was a chance of further cuts, Bull replied, "No. Well, I hope not." Refusing to be drawn into any discussion of the controversy's political and personal aspects, he said, "The entire matter is still under negotiation and basically, we are sitting tight."

Four months later, such circumspection no longer served a purpose. By July 11, papers like the *Montreal Star* were running stories under headlines reading, "Blame Ottawa Bungling as Space Shot Shelved." In a number of interviews, Bull blasted the government, and said "political meddling and intrigue" were responsible for the project falling two years behind schedule. He said there was now no hope that a satellite could be shot into orbit in 1967.

Terminally ill from financial anemia, HARP got its execution notice from the government early that November. C.M. Drury announced in the House that funding would cease as of June 30, 1967. Even the fact that the Scientific Secretariat of the Science Council of Canada was still carrying out its first major project, a detailed and painstaking review of Canada's space programs, didn't stop the government from pulling the plug. The rationale was that the investment was not paying off, in terms of job creation and export sales!

The government gave its large investment in the Allouette communications satellites, the $2,500,000-a-year expenditure on the Fort Churchill rocket-launch facility, and the expensive development of the Black Brant sounding rocket, as examples of projects that met these criteria. While it was true that these programs generated valuable sales of technology to the U.S., West Germany, and a host of other nations, by firms like RCA Canada, Bristol Aerospace, and De Havilland Aircraft, using them as a reason for dumping HARP missed the point. To say, as one official did, that HARP hadn't worked hard enough to sell "hardware and services," overlooks the fact that foreigners seldom buy technologies that the vendor's own government won't support, or is less than enthusiastic about.

Besides, as the government and its senior scientists knew well, the state of the technology didn't give the Space Research Institute that much to sell. Bull's plans for follow-on launchers—huge, purpose-built compound guns—needed verification by direct experiment, to prove their utility. If his jury-rigged, scrap-built, sixteen-inch launchers could orbit any sort of mass, it would lead the way to far heavier (around seven-hundred-pound) satellites, which could be launched cheaply, and in great numbers.

The reality was that not one of the government institutions involved with Canadian civilian or military scientific research would touch HARP follow-on projects, or show any desire to investigate applications for a gun-based, Canadian-built orbital capability. The National Research Council, heavily committed to the Fort Churchill rocket-launch installation, saw Bull as competition. What was left of DRB, the Ministry of Defence Production, and the minions of Industry, Trade and Commerce took their cues from Minister Drury, and opposed it on general principles. The Canadian military, convulsed from having to deal with the disastrous unification drive of Defence Minister Hellyer, had little time to listen to the clamor from its junior levels to fight for HARP.

The Canadian decision also had the effect of terminating U.S. army funding. As Charlie Murphy described it, "Our funding went through the Canadian government...so there was essentially one contract between them and McGill. When that one contract wasn't renewed, all money stopped."

So abrupt was the cancellation that a series of atmospheric firings at Yuma was still in progress. There was no way to even analyze the data already collected. Murphy was later able to get U.S. army funding to finish the study, since it was being done by a sub-contractor in Atlanta, and only "because this didn't touch McGill."

With its government support terminated, HARP quickly crumbled, and its support from industrial, and particularly university sources, dried up. The University of Toronto's Gordon Patterson, in his autobiography, *Pathway to Excellence*, referred to Gerry Bull as "one of my pioneering students of exceptional ability," and then offered this cool comment on the demise:

> As the Barbados project progressed it became evident that administrative problems were developing and that the very high cost of operating a launching facility relative to normal university resources was exerting a pressure against further involvement. I requested Dr. Glass [one of Bull's ex-professors] and Dr. deLeeuw to review the whole situation and recommend a course of action. It became clear from this review that at best the [University of Toronto Aerospace] Institute could only continue as a user of the Barbados gun launch facility. Subsequently technical difficulties were encountered in the design of [our] Institute's experiments arising from the very high launch acceleration, and funding problems devel-

oped. It was also becoming evident that the Canadian government would take over and operate the rocket launching facilities at Fort Churchill. Since this involved NRC support for university participation, the Institute's need for the Barbados range vanished.

Mimi Bull remembers the time, for reasons unrelated to Project HARP. "That was the year of the birth of my last child, Noemi Jean, on the seventh of July...She was premature, and I must say that I wasn't feeling very well. My husband kept very quiet about what was going on, so as not to disturb me." While her daughter would be fine, the birth had been a hard one, and Mimi spent that summer at the house in Highwater, recuperating from the delivery.

The press of events kept Gerry away from home for much of that year. The winding-down of the HARP project, which involved laying off most of the staff, and the temporary reduction of the facilities at Highwater and Barbados to caretaker status, took his attention. While the Space Research Institute at McGill had ceased to exist, as of July 1, 1967, Bull was left with a responsibility to a small group of McGill students who worked on HARP as a part of their still-unfinished postgraduate studies, and to the team of skilled workers he had assembled over the years.

As Murphy described it, "he was trying to find some other mechanism to keep his people together, so he formed an attachment with Norwich University in Northfield, Vermont, in December of 1967. He was with them for about a year or so...they gave him a framework for the graduate students at Highwater to continue their studies."

In late 1967, the Institute purchased a four-thousand-acre block of American land, directly south of the Highwater property. According to Murphy, "That was a vital part of the deal...he had the ties to a Vermont university, and that got him money from the state government for bringing in industry. He got the funding to build a new headquarters building on the property, near to the village of North Troy in Vermont."

This move expanded the Highwater site to some ten thousand acres. Surrounded, in both Canada and the United States, by a high fence patrolled by its own security force, it became an trans-border enclave. While a full-time customs officer from each country was paid by the institute to monitor what came in and out through the north and south gates, the practical effect was to turn it into a neutral zone, whose ambiguous status would only become apparent in the years ahead.

Bull also found that his new American base opened up new sources of funding. Murphy explained it this way. "There were a few minor U.S. army contracts, mostly from the Picatinny arsenal [but] his major cost support became U.S. navy, at that time. The work involved designing new long-range projectiles for fleet use, under the Gunfighter program. Some of these shells were used by eight-inch cruisers on fire-support missions off the coast of Vietnam...It was all done through Indian Head, the navy propellant plant in Maryland, just south of Washington. The navy hadn't done much research on guns in the past twenty years, and the Indian Head outfit was always on the verge of being closed down. They figured out that, gee whiz, they should expand into projectiles to keep from going out of business. With the HARP program they got real excited, since some of their guys had been down to Barbados and seen what Gerry could do for shell ranges...they got the admirals to come up with the money. The trouble was, both parties [Bull and Norwich] found it was very complicated running ordnance contracts through a small university."

This problem was to lead Bull into new realms. He had considered privatizing the Space Research Institute even before the HARP cancellation. The Institute had always been something of an anomaly in a university setting, and he had long realized that many of its functions were not suited to the structure of an educational institution. The nature of its programs meant it needed a manufacturing component, as distinct from basic research work, and running production facilities is not usually considered an academic function. The idea was reasonable, because the Institute had always led an independent existence. It was never a part of the traditional McGill structure—it had merely sheltered under its aegis.

Norwich University can be seen in the same perspective. It was a place to camp out, while Bull wrestled with the future shape of the Institute. Events quickly showed that administering a complex endeavor, with sites thousands of miles apart, was beyond the resources of a school with fewer than a thousand students and a faculty and staff of two hundred. This led Bull into the world of private enterprise, and the problems of dealing in a different *milieu*. While he had worked with scores of commercial firms over the years, it had been from the perspective of a government employee purchasing services, or a professor buying products for a university. Becoming a businessman was quite another thing, and there are those who say that Gerry Bull never really mastered the art.

The main deficiency he faced, at the start, was a lack of managerial people with the experience to structure the entity into a viable business, and run it as such. While turning a profit from the skills of the working groups he had managed to hold together was the objective, doing it required an outside infusion of money and skills. With the same verve he had applied to hustling grants for CARDE and HARP, Bull went looking for private investment. The pitch was that a firm handling Canadian and U.S. defense-research contracts and specialised electronics projects, and with the potential to be in the orbital-launch business, would be a profitable business.

It was a proposition with substance. Besides the considerable knowledge base and the initial U.S. navy contracts, there were research sites, equipment and supplies, some of them acquired at what Bull called "fire-sale prices." His skill as a pack rat, who constantly picked up gear that others had discarded, was aided by a Canadian government that, Bull claimed, was willing "to do anything to help get rid of me!" With these assets at hand, Bull soon found a number of small investors in Vermont and Québec who were willing to back him. Still, he needed a partner who could bring in the necessary business talent, as well as providing access to a larger pool of money and credit.

Great Western Saddlery, a firm that got its start in 1869, selling dry goods and making harnesses and saddles for the North-West Mounted Police, might seem a strange choice for this role of major partner. But, according to Peter C. Newman, in his 1978 book, *Bronfman Dynasty— The Rothschilds of the New World*, this once-prosperous company had been plundered by corporate raiders, so that it was merely a shell when Edward and Peter Bronfman took it over, in May of 1968. For the two scions of an extraordinary family, which made millions in the liquor business with its Seagram's distilleries, and then compounded it into billions with its later investments in oil, banking and insurance, it was a convenient vehicle for a new series of investments in real estate, hotels and high-technology industries. Directed by Paul Lownestein and Neil Baker, two exceptionally talented whiz-kids of the type the Bronfmans were so adept at hiring, Great Western Saddlery saw Bull and the Space Research Institute as a chance worth taking. In the fall of 1968, they took over the assets and liabilities of the Institute as majority owners, and set it up as a commercial venture, Space Research Corporation (SRC) of Vermont. Bull was appointed president, and the R.D. Little company of Boston was brought in to provide managerial experience.

The association with the Bronfmans proved to be a short one. Unlike the other high-tech investments that Great Western Saddlery had made, in firms like Aquila Computer Services, the quick return and equity build-up they were looking for were not available from SRC's operations. Bull's work methods did not sit well with Lownestein and Baker. The cost-paring, analytical approach of a corporation run by accountants, at the beck and call of distant masters, was equally disagreeable to Bull. A mutual recognition that the hasty marriage suited neither partner, made the separation an amicable one. According to Mimi Bull, "I don't think they stayed more than a year...Gerry bought it back."

It was at this point that SRC became two companies; SRC of Vermont, and SRC-Québec. While this made dealing with two nations easier, it was mainly a paper split. Bull ran SRC as one integrated operation throughout its life.

The Bull family will not comment on where the funds for the buy-out came from, but many who are familiar with the early days of SRC assume the Gilbert family assisted in guaranteeing at least a part of the bank loans required for the purchase. If they did, the investment was a good one, for SRC was off to a promising start. A Toronto *Globe and Mail* article of March 11, 1980, said that the company did $2 million worth of business in 1970, its first full year of operation. By 1971, it was employing 300 people and had an annual payroll of over $1.6 million.

Bull assembled an impressive board of directors for the new firm. The first was his old friend, General Arthur Trudeau. After retiring from the army in 1962, Trudeau had become president of Gulf Oil's Research and Development Company at Harmonville Texas, a position that lasted until July of 1968. He then took a variety of posts, ranging from a trustee of West Point Military Academy to Assistant to the Chairman of the Board of what is now Rockwell International. His accomplishments, and the prestige of his distinguished war record, gave him immense influence with the army's high command, It was a power he was to use to the maximum, in supporting SRC and Gerry Bull. Other board members included General Barksdale Hamlett, president of Norwich University; Sterling Cole, a former member of Congress, and once chairman of the Vienna-based International Atomic Energy Commission; and Dr. Jean de Valpine, of the Memorial Drive Trust.

Through privatization with the Bronfmans and the return to his own control, Bull still maintained a liaison with Norwich. According to Frank Griffith, a spokesman for the university, "He was carried on our staff as a part-time instructor, but he gave no classes here. Officially, the connection ended in 1974, but for all practical purposes, it ceased as of 1971."

One person who came into SRC from Norwich and stayed, was Rodgers Gregory. A retired army colonel, he had been an administrator at Norwich throughout the sixties, and Bull badly needed those types of skills. From his initial position as executive assistant to the SRC president, he would take an ever-increasing responsibility for the firm's operations in the years ahead.

Initially, most of this activity stemmed from its Indian Head contracts, and that required use of the Barbados site. With transportation assistance from the U.S. navy, a horizontal eight-inch gun was emplaced on the headlands of Foul Bay, and an open-air card range was set up to measure the behavior of the sleek new naval rounds. While the mighty, sixteen-inch, L83 barrel sat idle for most of this period (several firings of surplus Martlet projectiles, the year before, had used up the available powder charges), another huge barrel was implanted on the site. Charlie Murphy said, "He had got a program from the [U.S.] air force for impact studies on various materials, using the rifled, sixteen-inch horizontal gun he set up to shoot into targets."

The Aeroballistics Laboratory, as the Highwater site was now styled, remained the center of SRC's activities. New, more-permanent construction replaced many of the raw wood structures from the HARP days. Besides the sixteen-inch, limited-elevation tube, the low hills and scrub pine echoed to the crack of eight-inch and 155 millimetre cannons firing test shots. As part of the U.S. air force impact studies, a special light gas gun simulated micro-meteorite impacts. Driven by conventional explosives, a piston compressed helium gas which, in turn, fired lexan plastic pellets into the targets at over thirty thousand feet per second. In the new labs and machine shops of Highwater, busy technicians built precision models, constructed specialized electronic equipment, or calibrated sensor equipment for the ranges. The number of workers rose rapidly, as Bull garnered a steady stream of new research contracts from military sources. By 1972, Highwater employed almost four hundred people.

In September of 1970, SRC-Québec had received its first contract from the Canadian government. It was to conduct a top-secret study on "towed, underwater bodies" for a new class of variable-depth sonar systems. (Fluid dynamics, one of Bull's specialties, applies equally well to the behavior of objects in either air or water.) Designed to be trawled behind anti-submarine-warfare vessels, SRC's work would assist in keeping Canada a world leader in submarine hunting.

Some may find it strange that, after the CARDE affair and the demise of HARP, a government filled with Bull's "enemies" would give him work. The unique, cross-disciplinary body of expertise at SRC aside, not even those who loathed Bull could deny his brilliance or his ability to deliver "good data" from the most demanding research tasks. Besides, dealing with Bull as a supplier of services was a different thing from having to view him as a colleague or competitor in the confines of the bureaucracy. He was to get an increasing number of contracts from the Department of National Defence, right up to the eventual demise of SRC.

In 1971, Bull appointed long-time colleague William Friend as Vice-President and Technical Director of SRC-Québec, at the new head offices in Montréal. Friend, who graduated the University of Toronto in 1958, with a Master's in aeronautical engineering, went to CARDE, where he joined Bull's B Wing and specialized in developing equipment and experiments to simulate hypervelocity micro-meteorite impacts on space vehicles. Moving to McGill in 1961 as a lecturer, he joined the Space Research Institute in 1964, and worked on many aspects of the HARP program. Staying with the Institute through privatization, he would contribute much to SRC-Q's success in getting DND contracts, by scrupulous organization and the development of a line of training-munitions products. A few years later, he was to feel that his decades of loyalty to Gerry Bull and his work had been abused, perhaps even betrayed.

As the winter of 1971 spread its coat of snow over Highwater and the Bull estate, Mimi Bull remembers it as a time when their family life settled into what could almost be termed a routine. With SRC reorganized and the turmoil of privatization over, Bull was able to spend more time with family and friends. Increasingly, Highwater, rather than the house in Montréal, became the center of that social life. Not only was it a few minutes drive away from SRC's head office in Vermont, it provided Bull with easy access to many of the outdoor activities he enjoyed. While fishing, the interest that had brought him to Mimi Gilbert's door, was still a pleasure, it was now sports that could be done in a family group that took his interest.

Charlie Murphy and his wife, Betty, would often visit, with their children, and they and the Bulls would go skiing at nearby Jay Mountain resort. Other guests at the Highwater weekends included General Trudeau, his new wife, and members of the Bronfman family, particularly Paul Bronfman, who, Mimi says, "struck up quite a friendship with Gerry."

The new role of prosperous businessman seems to have suited Bull. Highwater became a stopping place for scientists, politicians and military men, who would be given the Cook's tour of the installation by Bull himself. For those he was especially trying to please, or just found interesting to talk to, a visit to his nearby house for dinner, drinks, and perhaps an overnight stay, was de rigueur. After a hearty meal, Bull would take his guests into the cavernous living room. There, before a blaze in the great stone fireplace with the moosehead above the mantle, he would wave his glass and sketch dreams of gigantic guns and space travel to his eminent visitors. Surely he must have reflected, at times, what a change it was from the days of a threadbare young scientist living in a Québec City boarding house.

The year 1972 brought a continuation of SRC's rapid—some would say too rapid—growth. Contracts, workloads and employment were rising quickly. The diversification that this brought into the company would later create problems, as it strained a management structure based largely on Bull's hands-on approach to everything. But, at the time, none of this was evident, and a bright future for SRC seemed assured.

That year, the high-angle L83 gun at Foul Bay was back in use for a short time. Sannu Molder, now a professor with the engineering department of Toronto's Ryerson Polytechnical Institute, came up with a unique use for a gun launcher—testing a SCRAMjet engine.

Supersonic Combustion RAMjets, as the name implies, are air-breathing thrusters, capable of burning fuel in an airflow traveling

faster than the speed of sound. Even though conventional turbine or RAMjet engines can produce supersonic flight, they must slow the airflow into the thrust chamber below sonic velocity, or the engine will flame out. The drag produced by this effect is what makes conventional supersonic flight so fuel-intensive, and effectively limits it to speeds below Mach 3.5. Such engines are theoretically capable of producing speeds of up to orbital velocity at Mach 25, and a SCRAMjet engine will power the American X-30 aerospace plane, currently under development by NASA.

The catch is that SCRAMjets will not function at speeds below Mach 3.5. This, plus the fact that their construction needs materials capable of withstanding fantastic heat, has limited their development for half a century. Beginning in 1964, when he was taking his Master's and Ph.D. programs at McGill, Molder began looking for a way to flight-test the SCRAM concept. In conjunction with the National Research Council (NRC), which tested the inlet geometries in its Ottawa wind tunnel and produced the actual test projectile, he designed the experiment. Fired as a saboted round from the L83, it was to burn for 1.5 seconds, resulting in a velocity increase of Mach 1.7 over the gun's muzzle velocity.

The project involved a close association with Gerry Bull throughout the HARP project and, to a lesser degree, during the early days of SRC, as well. Besides providing the first known attempt to actually fly a SCRAMjet, Bull saw it as a possible booster for the upper stages of his orbital gun-launchers. Molder worked with him both at Highwater and the Barbados site, which he visited a half-dozen times, including one trip when he flew down with Dean Donald Mordell in his private aircraft. He describes the early days of SRC as an environment where "people came and went...there was a lot of turnover...Gerry put a lot of pressure on some people; it was that kind of operation."

While Molder got on well with Bull (no doubt because he was pushing a very advanced idea), not all did. Gerry, as the driving force behind SRC's activities, would always listen to ideas, but he had no time for excuses, or people who didn't measure up to his standards. But, if Bull pushed people hard, he also pushed himself, for he knew that changing circumstances in the field of aeronautical research meant that SRC, for all its initial successes, would have to grow or die.

Charlie Murphy remembers the SCRAM project well, since Aberdeen cooperated with the NRC in funding Molder's experiment. Murphy was not happy with the results. "Molder managed to engineer it wrong...the damn things came apart after leaving the barrel."

As Molder recalls it, "The first shot suffered a sabot separation failure and tumbled...with the second one, the skin did peel off...but a fairly simple redesign would have solved that."

It was not to happen. Funding had run out for the SCRAM engine, and there were no new programs in either Canada or the United States that could make use of it. As he ruefully admits today, Molder was not the only aeronautical scientist to suffer such disappointment in those years.

The early 1970s marked a peak in aeronautical science, and the flow of money into it from government and corporate coffers. Strenuous efforts by universities had reduced the critical shortage of personnel in the 1950s to manageable levels, by the 1960s. By the time the seventies rolled around, there was a positive glut on the market. Molder describes it as "the end of the hypersonics era...We had been to the moon, and the pressure was off. Funding for our science dried up."

Murphy defined it in terms of success leading to the end of many basic science programs started in the 1950s. "The information was in, so the jobs were out."

Public pressures for more spending on social programs, and the desire of governments to spend money in other, equally useful scientific fields, also contributed to the decline. If the golden age of aeronautical science had come to an end, so, in a sense, had Gerry Bull's scientific career. Addressing it from that perspective, Molder summed up twenty years of Bull's work with, "I left McGill, and my close association with Gerry ended at that time...he was at the apex of his career...his apogee was sometime in 1970...I was not in touch with him during his downward trajectory."

In view of events to come, only a scientist would define it that way. It was true, however, in the sense that there would be no more basic breakthroughs like gun-fired models and instrumented shells. For Gerry Bull had become a businessman and, in spite of himself, he was now a user of science, not a developer of it. While his outlooks on technology, and the way it was institutionalizing itself in the Western world, would continue to grow, he reverted back to what he had always been at heart, a person who made things, an *engineer*.

Opinions vary on what effect the death of HARP, and the interregnum following it, had on the outlook of Gerry Bull. Mimi says it was minimal. "I think it just confirmed thoughts that he already had." *Hardened* might be a better description. No matter how vehemently he might proclaim it in later years, Bull was no longer a Canadian nationalist. It would be fifteen years before he would openly reveal his disgust with the nation of his birth, but his actions spoke long before that.

Sannu Molder recalls that Gerry's dream of orbiting satellites by gunfire had not died in 1972. Indeed, they had grown even bigger. He often spoke to Molder about what he referred to as the Kwajalein gun, and his desire to somehow get funding for it. Named after a remote, American-controlled Pacific atoll, 4,500 kilometers southwest of Hawaii, the launcher was to be emplaced on the island of Taongi, in a tightly restricted area used as a ballistic-missile target range for rockets fired from distant Vandenberg air force base, in California.

As early as 1964, Bull began planning the follow-on to Project HARP; a series of cannons so gigantic that they would make the L83, with its 110-foot barrel, look like a mere hunting rifle beside them. One design called for a sectional, smooth-bore tube with a one-meter interior diameter. But the ultimate was something to rival the fantasies of Jules Verne in *From Earth to the Moon*. A sixty-four-inch cannon, with an eight-hundred-foot, six-thousand-ton barrel, would be supported on a giant cradle held up to the sky by a seventy-story skyscraper. As Bull ultimately conceived it, no mere high explosive would propel its shells into space. Instead, a turbulent mix of liquid hydrogen and oxygen would be detonated in a charge chamber, sealed off from the tube by a super-quick shutter that would snap open an instant after detonation. Every shot of this stupendous bombard would deliver six tons into low earth orbit. In less than two months, it could orbit more mass than all the rockets ever fired into space.

Just what sort of payloads would be fired from a super-secret military base became a persistent question. First raised by peace activists at McGill in 1965, it was to resurface whenever Bull's Kwajalein gun came up—was it really a plan for mass deployment of nuclear weapons in space?

People differ on what was really involved in the project, and how far it got. Charlie Murphy dismisses it as never going "much beyond the idea stage," and denies it had anything to do with atomic bombs.

However, SRC board member Sterling Cole had a different story to tell. In a 1978 interview with reporter Sam Hemmingway, of Vermont's *Burlington Free Press*, he linked the Kwajalein gun with nuclear weapons, and another significant event in Gerry Bull's life.

"Rare Act of Congress Aided Space Research Chief," was the title of the article, in which Cole mentioned the "revolutionary concept" of gun-launching nuclear warheads into orbit, to "knock out Soviet spy satellites." He also said the plan could orbit hundreds of nuclear warheads, as a deterrent against the Soviet Union's rapidly expanding strategic missile force!

SRC research on hyper-velocity impacts, for the U.S. air force, had already given Bull access to very sensitive information on the construction of inter-continental nuclear warheads. Studies of the Kwajalein gun, involving a possible nuclear role, meant access to more such data. As a federal immigration officer, familiar with Bull's citizenship case, put it, the American government realized it had "goofed on clearance," giving Bull access to information that their laws said only U.S. citizens could possess.

To cover up the mistake, a private bill was passed in the U.S. Senate in October 1972, which waived the residency requirements for

Bull to become an American citizen. It was sponsored by one-time presidential candidate and Republican senator from Arizona, Barry Goldwater. Also speaking in favor of the extraordinary proposal was George Aiken, a Republican senator from Vermont, and James Eastland, a Democratic member from Mississippi.

Bull's U.S. citizenship was granted on January 22, 1973, one day after the shortened waiting period expired. According to the immigration source, the hearing, in the Vermont District Court in Brattleboro, was conducted with "an extreme sense of haste." Bull and his character witnesses had to wait several hours, while Judge James Oakes of the Second U.S. Circuit Court of Appeals, in New York, was flown in specially for the unscheduled session.

With the citizenship issue safely behind him, Bull plunged into ever-more-secret American military research. However, the plan for the Kwajalein gun quickly faded away from a lack of money for even prototype studies. As Murphy explained it, "The air force was wedded to rocket launch systems," and the idea of a Fractional Orbital Bombardment System (FOBS), no matter what launched it, would have required abrogation of U.S.-Soviet treaties from the mid-sixties, which prohibited the orbiting of nuclear weapons. Cole said the military "shut them (Space Research) down," and he called the termination a "great tragedy for national security."

As the collapse of the Cold War shows us today, it was anything but a disaster for the safety of the American nation, and the rest of the planet, as well. But it was a tragedy for Bull. The potentially brilliant idea of a cheap way into space had gone down in flames, once more. Stillborn, the Kwajalein project put paid to the last serious hope for "Bull's pipe dream" in North America. Two-time losers in the scientific sweepstakes seldom get a third try. Their ideas become like the stories in pulp science magazines about the imminent return of the Zeppelin—they still sound good, but they never happen.

Not that Bull gave up. For years to come, no matter where the twists of fortunes took him, the dream remained a stubborn obsession. Submerged, hidden by the yearly progression of events, it would surface in vastly different circumstances, fifteen years later.

Concurrent with what seemed to be the death of the HARP concept, another, equally significant change of direction took place in Bull's career. Research was what SRC had been doing and, while it did it very well, Gerry was, no doubt, well aware of the wisdom in Murphy's crack about "the information was in, so the jobs were out." Basic research contracts only last so long, and the fields are quickly harvested. To survive, Bull and SRC had to come up with products that used their particular skills.

CHAPTER 9

"Artillery is the God of War."

—Joseph Stalin

After a few drinks, artillerymen often claim that they, not prostitutes, are the world's oldest profession. The argument is based on the contention that there is no difference between the mental calculations of a caveman hurling a rock, and the mathematics required for a gun to bombard a target forty kilometers away.

One does not have to go that far to understand that artillery is an ancient art. Gunpowder, a mixture of charcoal (carbon), sulphur and saltpeter, was known to the Chinese as early as 1,000 B.C., but they never invented the weapon that would give it its name. It is not known who first got the idea of putting this primitive explosive in a tube, sealed at one end, and using it to propel a ball of rock or metal in the direction of a foe, but history suggests it was an Arab. Before the end of the first millennium A.D., the Caliphs of Baghdad are known to have used a form of cannon, called *manjaniks*, in their wars with the Persians.

The impact of artillery on human affairs was to be tremendous. Some historians claim it was the major factor in the destruction of European feudalism. Since constructing the weapons demanded more organization and manpower than most errant nobles could raise, bombards meant the strongest castle of a robber baron was now vulnerable to the growing central authority of the European states. By the time of the French Revolution and the Napoleonic wars, artillery had, by a slow process of improvement, truly become "the God of War." While gallant, and often suicidal, cavalry charges caught the attention of iconographers and artists of the period, it was massed batteries of guns that usually won the battles. Napoleon was an artilleryman, and his use of the weapon in both static and mobile warfare contributed as much to his dizzying record of conquest as the élan of the French soldiers, who carried his flags as far afield as Egypt and Moscow.

With the coming of the industrial age, the ancient weapon gained new and more powerful attributes. Breech-loading mechanisms, and the development of high-strength steels for barrels, relegated the familiar muzzle-loaders, with their round cannon balls, to the history books. Rifled tubes, which spin-stabilized their cylindrical, pointed shells, took over. New, "smokeless," nitrocellulose-based explosives, such as cordite, not only cleared the battlefield of "the fog of war" produced by black powder, they were more energetic propellants that extended gun range far beyond the visible. The result was the end of limited war, and the concept that such struggles were best waged by small military elites. Future conflicts would be waged with the products of the assembly line, and the total commitment of national resources.

It was an era that historians describe as the age of the cannon kings. Krupp in Germany, the Schneiders in France, and Vickers in Great Britain—all grew rich on the deadly products of the forge. In the late nineteenth and early twentieth centuries, no World Fair or International Exhibition was complete without the showing of some stupendous, fat-barrelled bombard, to draw the admiration of the masses. Combined with rising nationalism and the medieval dreams of European leaders, who did not comprehend what technology had wrought, these weapons led to the slaughter of World War I. While the bloodbath involved huge masses of men, it was the heavy gun, more than all the rifles, machine guns and landmines put together, that slew them in their millions.

For victors and vanquished alike, the Great War saw the apogee of the heavy artillery piece and the lighter field gun as the main arm of conflict. In the next World War, tanks, aircraft, and electronics would diminish, but by no means eliminate, the cannon from its role as king of the battlefield. From El Alamein to Stalingrad and the great Soviet offensives of 1944-45, massed guns and thousands of tons of shells smashed defenses and blew gaping holes in German lines, which allowed allied troops and armor to pour through to victory.

By the end of the second global conflict, and with the dawning of the missile age, fundamental research on heavy guns disappeared. In the fifties and sixties, as the great powers developed global-reach missiles and thousands of atomic weapons that they dared not use, artillery development lacked glamour—and funding. What work there was, concentrated on piecemeal improvements, such as better-burning propulsive charges and more sophisticated fuses for airburst munitions. While sophisticated ranging and fire-control systems made the effect of gun batteries more devastating, little real improvement in range or individual weapon accuracy occurred.

Ignored though its form and development might have been, the gun remained the prime determinant on Third World battlefields, from Korea to the Iraq-Iran war. Even in conflicts considered as guerrilla struggles, the cannon still spoke. The 1952 French disaster at Dien Bien Phu, which forced them to withdraw from Indo-China, was a direct result of losing an artillery battle with Ho Chi Minh's Viet Minh gunners.

In the West, guns with a reach of up to fifteen kilometers became the standard by the 1950s. In the Eastern Bloc, tubes with about a twenty percent range advantage over their Western counterparts were developed. American and allied armed forces accepted this imbalance, calculating that superior airpower would turn the tables in the mythical, World War III battle for Europe.

Yet, East or West, the cannon remained a product of nineteenth-century engineering. Gerry Bull underscored this, when describing a revolutionary new gun that SRC began developing in the early 1970s. "There's nothing new there...nothing a gunner from a century ago wouldn't instantly recognize."

While, in one sense, that is true, the Victorian artilleryman would stand in awe of Bull's creation. No wide-snouted, ponderous muzzle here; instead, a slender, almost-delicate barrel,capable of being elevated to 75 degrees. Weighing 13.5 metric tons, it rides on four pneumatic tires, arranged on a classically simple, split-trail mount. Named the GC-45, this mighty, 155mm gun/howitzer meets the ultimate test of engineering ability—to the specialist, it looks profoundly right. With more accuracy, increased range and greater weight of shell, it still outshoots anything in its class today.

Bull said the secret of his success was to apply "high-technology design principles to a low-technology weapon...I treated shell, barrel and [charge] chamber as a synchronous whole...which pushed efficiency towards the theoretical limits." He stressed that the previous generations of artillery designers tended to build guns to fit existing shell configurations and, in trying to keep the shell as cheap and simple as possible, seemed blind to the possibilities of aerodynamic design. In describing his new Extended Range, Full Bore (ERFB) projectiles, custom designed for the GC-45, he said, "previous shells were designed to travel down a gun barrel. I built mine to fly through the air."

When it came to developing a product to sell, the GC-45 was an eminently logical one. It made use of two decades of experience in projectile design and gun-barrel technology. From the University of Toronto wind tunnel, through the CARDE experience, to the aeroballistic projectiles of the HARP launchers, the GC-45 design process became an almost seamless progression. Combined with the extended-range, 155mm shell for standard artillery that SRC began testing in 1972, and the business trips Bull began making to Europe and the Middle East, the linkage becomes complete.

The first series of visits to Europe, in 1972 and 1973, was directly related to promoting his new shell. Preceded by his international reputation in ballistics, he was able to tour shell-production facilities in England, France, West Germany, the Netherlands and Belgium. There, he discussed possible manufacturing arrangements, and gained an understanding of European manufacturing techniques and capabilities. He also arranged firing demonstrations of shell prototypes, before military and corporate leaders, at various artillery ranges. One problem he ran into was that the projectile was so efficient, many European ranges were not big enough to allow the new aeroballistic round to be safely fired. According to a Canadian artillery specialist, standard shells, fired from weapons like the American M-109, thirty-nine-caliber gun, "reach to seventeen kilometers, if you have a strong wind at your back."

In the same gun, Bull's shell—with the addition of a technical development that will be mentioned shortly—reached twenty-two kilometers, and was far more accurate. Ironically, this made it difficult to get time slots on the few available ranges, and it was harder to persuade observers to travel long distances to view the shots.

While artillerymen were enthusiastic when they saw the results, the major European manufacturers were less so. Bull was to discover that the old saw about the world beating a path to your door when you build a better mousetrap doesn't apply to armaments sales in the First World. Through most of his attempts to sell the extended-range shell, and later, during the effort to market the GC-45, this paradox was to come back to haunt him again and again.

Strangely, independent corporate innovation has little to do with the development of modern weapons. While companies are encouraged to research and develop technologies, the reality of the process actively discourages them from making unsolicited proposals for systems that take advantage of it. The defense industries generally wait until military and government bureaucracies decide there is a *requirement* for a system to meet given objectives. No requirement, no market; so why bother?

Another part of the process was to bedevil Bull for the rest of the decade. Next to the political realities of available funding, the prime drive in formulating a requirement is the fighting doctrine of the armed force that will use the weapon. "The wrench must fit the nut," is how the supporters of the process define it. Others say this approach is what keeps armies buying the latest tools to fight the last war with. As an example, U.S. army field doctrine, at the time, regarded targets beyond a thirty-kilometer range as an air-force responsibility, so there was no possible requirement for a gun, such as the GC-45, that could shoot beyond that range.

The incestuous ties between national governments and their home suppliers of armaments is another factor that discourages the innovator, especially if he is a foreigner. A former executive with Space Research, who played a major role in the ammunition development for the GC-45, explains it this way. "N.I.H. syndrome—that stands for Not Invented Here—is a standard procedure, especially in countries like the U.S., U.K., France, and Germany, which have their own indigenous capabilities. It's especially true in the ammunition field. What incentive did these companies have to buy our shell design? They already had their contracts, and to use Gerry's round, they would have had to re-tool and pay us licensing fees. We were frozen out."

But if Bull found no takers in the big leagues, there were those in Europe's second rank who took an interest. Smaller companies, hungry for business, and with potential clients far beyond Europe, were willing to talk. To meet them, it was only natural that Bull would go to Brussels.

Belgium, by virtue of its small size and its pivotal geographic position amidst powerful neighbors, has always been a major crossroad of Western Europe. The site of many international organizations, such as NATO and the European Economic Community, its capital is an ideal place to develop contacts on a multi-national basis. It has also gained a reputation as a country where foreign defense companies can quietly take care of international business that might be an embarrassment at home.

In 1972, Bull demonstrated his shells at the Matagne and Kaulille facilities of a company called Poudre Reunion de la Belgique(PRB). PRB was a small, but long-established, munitions maker that produced a wide variety of tank and artillery shells, hand grenades, land mines and explosives for both the Belgian army and the export trade. Once closely associated with Fabrique National, the biggest and best-known of Belgian defense contractors, new management and declining sales were to take PRB into uncharted and dangerous waters.

Gerry Bull was fated to go with them, for PRB held the international marketing rights for another revolutionary development that none of the big-league players would touch. Base Bleed technology, as it is known, was originally a Swedish concept. A simple idea, it effectively solves a paradox that has frustrated artillery designers for over a century.

In a modern gun, the back of an artillery shell must be flat, to withstand the enormous force of the propellant explosion. Otherwise, even a projectile body of the strongest metal will be squeezed and deformed as it travels up the tube. Unfortunately, a flat back is a terrible aerodynamic shape for the rear body of a high-speed projectile, once it leaves the gun. It not only slows the shell down, it decreases its accuracy. Previous attempts at coming up with tricky shapes to solve the dilemma did not work, or else were too expensive to be practical.

A Base Bleed unit consists of a slow-burning powder charge at the rear of the shell, which ignites as it leaves the barrel. It is not a propulsive charge. The hot gases simply fill in the rear drag vortex, simulating an aerodynamic fairing that automatically adjusts to a wide variety of speeds. This increases the range of the shell by a third, and makes it more accurate at maximum range.

For both parties, the mating of Base Bleed and the aeroballistic projectile seemed a marriage made in technical heaven. Several research and development programs, to exploit the potential of the new supershell, were quickly worked out. To manage these activities, and to explore the possibilities of future ventures, a jointly owned, Belgian-registered company was formed—Space Research Corporation International (SRC-I).

In light of its pivotal role in activities that would later gain Bull international attention, it is strange that this company would be more misunderstood and misrepresented by the media than any other facet of Bull's operations. While it never actually produced anything on its own, SRC-I was to be the hub of a whole series of clandestine operations. It was the contractual vehicle and the major means of effecting technology exchanges between PRB, SRC-Q, and their customers.

Press files from the era reveal wide discrepancies about the supposed date of its founding (usually given as 1976) and who really controlled it. Even the subsequent American congressional investigations would fail to appreciate SRC-I's importance in the overall scheme of things. The strict Belgian law about releasing information on private firms is one cause of the confusion; the disinformation spread by Gerry Bull, his partners and associates, is another.

One thing is certain. Canadian Department of National Defence (DND) records show that the company was in existence as early as May of 1973. That month, DND funded a SRC-I presentation, which included demonstration models of the new technology, to a secret panel at

NATO Headquarters in Brussels, under the title, Extended Range Ammunition for 155mm Weapons—A Ballistic Solution.

Gerry's son, Michael, can be forgiven for having an imperfect knowledge of these events, since he was only seventeen in 1973. That fall, he was to enrol as a first-year student in biology at Montréal's Concordia University. However, in light of his subsequent services as an executive of a resurgent SRC-I, in the 1980s, his views on the subject are enlightening, if contradictory. In a 1987 interview with researcher Dyllon Roach, Michael vehemently claimed that SRC-Québec had been the majority owner of SRC-I, and that anything else "is a damned lie." He described the corporation as having been fifty-one-percent owned by SRC-Q, four percent by "private shares," and the remaining forty-five percent by PRB. Reports, based on South African sources, have claimed that it was fifty-five percent PRB, and only forty-five percent SRC-Q. In conversations in 1990, Michael would say it was fifty-one percent PRB, forty-five percent SRC-Q, and four percent "minority interests." Company letters and contracts relating to SRC-I activities, obtained from Austrian court records, confirm Michael's later recollection.

However, as much as the technologies might have complemented one another, the relationship between Gerry Bull and PRB was to be anything but friendly. Joseph Severin, who was PRB's president at the time, has been described as "a terrible man, whose only interest was money." While no one he worked with liked him, some, with good reason, were terrified of his threats and rages. Ruthless and immoral, he was a shark who made no pretense of hiding what he was.

But the man was to overreach himself. Events would shortly prove that he was too clever by half, and too greedy to be a success. Even in the cut-throat environment of the Brussels arms trade, successful business practice calls for accommodation and compromise in one's own interest. Severin would not admit that. His ego drove him to see business dealings as an arena, where eating opponents was more important than signing deals. In a few years, he would blow the best chance PRB and SRC ever had for getting large-scale, legitimate production of the GC-45 underway. Eurometal, a large, multi-national consortium, backed off from the proposed deal, when Severin demanded unrealistic amounts of money and control for PRB.

Asked if PRB's actions over the Eurosystems (the parent company of Eurometal) fiasco had harmed his father's credibility in Europe, Michael Bull said, "Absolutely...they were very hard to do business with...they had no ethics."

Such was the company that provided Gerry Bull's introduction to the shadowy world of second- and third-rank arms-dealing that had grown up in the complaisant atmosphere of Brussels. Ranging from billionaires to shabby men in backstreet buildings, scores of international arms-merchants had offices there. To this day, it is still a land of middlemen, "consultants", rumor-peddlers, and the fringe members of a dozen foreign intelligence agencies. In the vicious competition for deals and profits, men fight paper wars over the means to wage conflicts in some distant, Third World nation. The Brussels arms bazaar is a place where, behind closed doors on quiet streets, Israelis do business with Arabs, capitalists haggle with communists, and no one gives it a second thought.

One of the first members of this dark community whom Bull met in Brussels was an arms broker named Jacques Heymans. A native of Belgium, he got his start in the business by setting up arms routes into the Belgian Congo (now Zaire), in the late 1950s. Paid for by the Union Minere mining company, these weapons went to white mercenaries, fighting in the Katangese rebellion that was finally squashed by U.N. forces. A person who had already steered more than one sale to PRB, Heymans often boasted of his connections to prominent businessmen, government officials, military men and senior intelligence chiefs in a variety of nations.

One of the better connections Heymans possessed was a Tel-Aviv businessman named Shoul Eisenberg. In February of 1985, the Austrian newsmagazine, *Profil*, said he was one of the most influential middlemen in the Middle East and the Pacific area. "Without Eisenberg, nothing rolls," is how one of their sources put it. Reputed to be worth some $1 billion, Eisenberg, who holds dual Austrian and Israeli citizenship, is widely known as "Mr. Five Percent," referring to his standard commission on any deal he does. A secretive man, who seldom leaves Israel these days, Eisenberg has attracted controversy in more than one nation. In 1966, he was the subject of a Canadian parliamentary investigation over his role in the sale of Candu nuclear reactors to South Korea. Their report alleged that Eisenberg made a $5-million cut on the deal, plus $8 million in expenses, most of which was spent on bribing members of the South Korean government. Other sources say the payoffs ran as high as $25 million.

On Saturday, October 6, 1973—the Jewish holy day of Yom Kippur—the fragile cease-fire that had passed for peace between Israel and it's Arab neighbors since the Six-Day War of 1967, was shattered. Backed by the roar of four thousand guns and rocket launchers, a resurgent Egyptian army launched a surprise attack against the Bar-Lev line, on the east bank of the Suez Canal.

Eighteen days later, Israel would bring the conflict to a successful, if not completely victorious, conclusion by surrounding the Egyptian Fifth Army in the deserts both east and west of the canal. But, stunned as the Israelis might have been by the initial Egyptian assault, it was Syrian moves that gave the country's leadership its worst moments during the conflict. In concert with the Egyptian attack, a flood of

Soviet-supplied armor debouched from the Golan Heights, overlooking northern Israel. While the battles in the south took place in empty desert, a Syrian breakthrough from these dominating heights would have placed them amidst major Israeli population centers. Though the line was held by massive air strikes and the last-moment arrival of two tank brigades, the casualty figures were enormous for such a small country.

The Israeli government quickly decided that the situation could never be allowed to repeat itself. A counter-attack, in the closing days of the war, seized much of this Syrian territory, so that it could not be a springboard for future assaults. Yet the implementation hour of a Soviet and U.S.-backed United Nations ceasefire resolution left them short of their preferred stop line. Not only had their conquests remained a salient into Arab territory, but the objective of bringing Damascus and its ring of military bases into artillery range, was not achieved.

The Israelis regarded this as a strategic imbalance that left them potentially vulnerable to another attack. They also saw it as denying them the crucial negotiating card of a threat to Damascus that did not involve committing their air force over a deadly thicket of missile defenses. Since a U.N. buffer zone and a multi-national observer force now separated the two belligerents, further military action was not feasible. The Israeli military command was left with a dilemma to which some other solution would have to be found.

The answer came from the parastatal arms company, Israeli Military Industries (IMI). They suggested a way be found to increase the reach of their long-range 175mm guns from thirty to forty-five kilometers.

Besides selling nuclear power plants, Shoul Eisenberg also arranged arms deals, and one of the companies he dealt with was Israeli Military Industries. That was how the connection was made between the strategic needs of the Golan Heights and a company the ex-SRC executive called "a small bunch of guys out in the bloody woods of Québec." In a series of meetings between Bull, Heymans and Eisenberg, a rough deal was hammered out, and direct technical discussions with IMI were initiated. Sometime in November of 1973, Bull made at least two trips to Israel, to discuss how his new projectile could fit their needs.

The Israeli experts were impressed with Bull's solution to their quandary. To get the range, he suggested using his existing shell as a saboted round to be fired out of their American-built, M-107 175mm cannon. This rather inaccurate weapon normally fired a heavy shell out to thirty kilometers, the U.S. army's doctrinal limit. Loaded with Bull's saboted round, it would hurl the lighter, highly accurate 155mm shell to almost forty-five kilometers, far enough to reach Damascus and all the ports in southern Lebanon.

Israeli government approval of the project came quickly, but the problem of how to manufacture the fifty thousand shells they needed, remained. SRC didn't have the means to do it—all they had produced was a few hundred prototypes, prepared with the assistance of a U.S. army shell-forging plant in Scranton, Pennsylvania.

Here is where the often-two-level nature of arms dealing came to the fore. Call the Belgian connection, with its furtive meetings and shadowy possibilities, the low route. With a firm deal established, Israel and SRC were now free to take the high road; the lobbying of the U.S. and Canadian governments to approve the manufacture of the shells in North America.

For both partners, the means of accomplishing this was to be the American Central Intelligence Agency. From the Israeli side, it was a perfect time to ask a favor, since they had just provided the C.I.A. with a rich harvest of Soviet weaponry captured in the Yom Kippur War. There was no problem from the political side, either. American support of Israel was then at its zenith, and the picture of the Zionist state as a doughty little David, fighting the Arab Goliath, was still widely accepted.

From the SRC perspective, it was also an excellent way to go about it, for Bull and his board of directors had some first-class connections with the C.I.A.. General Arthur Trudeau had served as chief of U.S. army intelligence between 1953 and 1955 and, retired or not, that made him a permanent and knowledgeable member of the American intelligence community. He went all out, to support Gerry Bull's first big sale. Colonel Harry Bailley, who helped coordinate the American army's support of the project, was quoted in the September 12, 1979, issue of *The Burlington Free Press*, as saying, "Trudeau had a substantial role to play in favoring SRC...It seems to me that was his big bug."

Sterling Cole, through his Washington law practice and his past positions in government, also brought his considerable influence to bear. He had the ear of Henry Kissinger, and that helped gain the high-level support in the State Department that was essential to the deal's approval.

To produce the shells quickly, SRC needed to use the U.S. army forging plant in Scranton, but that presented some difficulties. American law forbade the use of such facilities by private contractors not selling directly to the army. A way was found around this, by bending the regulations so that SRC appeared to be acting only as "an agent" of the Israeli government. However, SRC was never listed as an agent of Israel by the Foreign Agents Registration Board of the U.S. Justice Department. Nor were the contracts involved registered under the Foreign Military Sales Act, as the law required.

The Canadian involvement in this affair was minimal, but the required government approvals came quickly when it was found that the project was supported by senior American officials. While the shells were forged and machined in American plants, the sabots were manufactured and mated to the projectiles in the Canadian part of the Highwater facility. In and out of the country, and they never left SRC's compound at all.

By the middle of 1974, the first shipments were on their way to Israel, via the Port of New York. Arriving at IMI's factory, the empty rounds were filled with explosives and the fuses provided. Before Yom Kippur rolled around again, Palestine Liberation Organization (PLO) bases near the Lebanese port of Sidon were suddenly struck by a short, but deadly, rain of fire and steel. From far beyond the range of any normal gun, artillery barrages wrecked supply depots, barracks and training areas, as well as killing and wounding scores of innocent civilians living in the area.

The debris had not stopped burning when the Syrian generals in Damascus received the message. Not only were their military bases threatened, but their very homes and offices were now in range of Gerry Bull's shells. Israeli media analysts soon noticed that the statements of the Syrian leadership against Israel became far less bellicose.

It's implementation buried beneath the highest security classifcations, the operation would later be represented in the media as the first of Bull's "C.I.A.-directed operations," and "the first time he worked for the Agency." As we have seen, reality was more prosaic and considerably more complex. The C.I.A. neither planned nor initiated the transfer. For its own purposes, it lent its clout and protection to a commercial transaction that conformed to American government policy of the time. In retrospect, they may have regretfully realized that they had provided Bull with a "in" to the many and varied official agencies of the American government, which would linger far beyond its original mandate.

With commissions and "expenses" added in, the deal cost the Israeli treasury upwards of $30 million. How much Gerry Bull and SRC actually got of that is not known, but it was undoubtably one of the smaller of many slices. For, while SRC had produced the design and Bull the concept, they were just one player in the game. The ad hoc nature of the manufacturing operation, wrapped as it was in secrecy and obscuration, made it an expensive expedient, one the Israelis were loath to repeat.

Here, SRC ran into a problem that many small companies with an innovative technology face—the customer likes the product so much that they don't want to buy it through the developer anymore; they want to acquire the right to build it themselves. Worse, they want to buy the licensing rights with a one-time payment, so there will be no royalties.

The next approach by Israel to SRC was precisely that, though it was sweetened with a final order for fifteen thousand unsaboted 155mm shells. Quoted by *The Burlington Free Press*, in 1979, an SRC official involved in the exports said, "Heymans negotiated the deal with Eisenberg and IMI. If the fifteen thousand units were purchased, Israel received a free license to manufacture the shells...The contract was a real weirdie. When I heard about it at the time, I said, 'Anybody can sell ten-dollar bills for five bucks.'"

That is exactly what SRC was forced to do by its partners. The company, in spite of the first big sale, was in a desperate financial state. The original wave of military-research contracts, which had sustained the company in its early years, had dried up.

The attempts to market the long-range shell in Europe had consumed several million dollars, without any return at all. SRC needed money, and Bull had no alternative.

The same lobbying process, the same pattern of regulation-bending, commenced again in late 1974. This time, however, an additional problem arose. American policy on arms sales to Israel had changed. To put pressure on the Jewish state to get moving on negotiations with its Arab neighbors, Henry Kissinger froze arms transfers to the Israeli armed forces. This was formalized in a U.S. Defense Department directive, in April 1975, which temporarily barred any new sales.

It only took SRC and it's allies a month to get around that one. A munitions-control-list license, issued to SRC on May 16, said Israel actually intended to re-sell the projectiles to the army of the Shah of Iran! It was a bald-faced lie, and one that should have been seen as a disturbing sign. The first time they had merely bent the rules; now they had bent the policy of the American government.

Some did begin to see the problem. While the original deal had aroused no opposition, voices in the various bureaucracies involved started to question the wisdom of giving SRC so much slack. An internal U.S. army memo, dealing with the operation, sounded a prescient warning. After stating that the sale represented a "substantial departure from past policy," it went on to say, "Special handling of the SRC request will set a precedent for future similar requests."

CHAPTER 10

If there was one thing Gerry Bull should have learned from the Israeli experience, it was that the best security and the most clever cover plan for an arms deal does not change the fact that technological secrecy is a transitory state of affairs. No introduction of technology into the Middle East, which affects the balance of power, goes unnoticed for long.

Beginning with the Arabic press, journalists began to ask questions about the deadly, new, Israeli weapon. Like a ripple, the story of the technology transfer began to spread. Given the global nature of the modern media, it was less than a year after the bombardment of Sidon that the story was being featured in Calypso songs in far-off Barbados. What, the lyrics asked, was a black nation doing playing host to a company that armed Zionist aggressors against fellow, Third World peoples?

Even without these tales, SRC's reputation in the Caribbean was already sinking. By 1975, popular opinion about their operations had undergone a dramatic shift in Barbados. Where Project HARP, with its civilian-oriented goals, had aroused no controversy and much support, the role of SRC, in using Barbados to test weaponry and develop ballistic-missile warhead technologies, was less appreciated. A growing left-wing movement, grouped around the Barbados Labour Party, soon found SRC's activities were a convenient stick with which to beat the conservatively oriented government of Errol W. Barrow.

Another dilemma was that the HARP installations had not been sited with security in mind. No matter how low a profile SRC might wish to keep, they were stuck beside a major airport, where their activities could be seen and heard from miles away.

Carlton Braithwaite, the Mr. Fix-it of the HARP days, was still with Bull, as General Manager of SRC's Barbados activities. Part of his job was to keep in touch with political developments on the island, and to try to influence them in SRC's favor. A practical man, Braithwaite soon came to the conclusion that the tide was running against the company. He was among the first to suggest that SRC go looking for somewhere else to base their testing operations.

The tiny island-nation of Antigua, 450 miles northwest of Barbados, was an ideal choice. Less sophisticated than Barbados, and desperate for investment, it approved the establishment of a new SRC, "operations test site," in 1975. But not without question. The U.K. was still responsible for its one-time colony's defense, and the government of Prime Minister Vere Bird asked London about the company.

Cosmos Phillips, an Antiguan lawyer, was the island's attorney-general in 1976. Later, he was to complain bitterly about the reassurances Antigua had received. "The government was badly treated," he told the Toronto *Globe and Mail*, for their March 10, 1980, issue. "It asked for the advice of the foreign office in London about Space Research. It asked the Canadian government and the U.S. government. And all three countries, big countries, told Antigua, a small country, not to worry. They all gave Space Research a clean bill of health.

"The Premier asked for their advice because there were intimations of illegal international arms deals when negotiations were going on for the company to come here."

While the fledgling government signed a secret agreement with SRC, granting it exemption from the island's immigration and customs laws, so that, for "reasons of security," it could bring in observers and equipment without the government's knowledge, the deal was not all one-sided. Besides lavish spending on hiring local lawyers and businessmen as "advisors" to lobby the government, SRC promised jobs and investment and, in a sense, it delivered. In return for being granted what were virtually extra-territorial rights on a deserted point known as Crab's Peninsula, on the other side of the island from its port and capital of St John's, SRC agreed to raise, train, and equip an army for Antigua.

What that meant, in effect, was that Gerry Bull acquired a private army, and his own internal security police. Known as the Antiguan

Defence Force, the three-hundred-man group was equipped with rifles, light machine guns and sporty black berets. Their real role was to guard Crab's Peninsula from curious eyes.

Impressive as it might sound, there is, in retrospect, an almost childish air of unreality about the operations of the Antiguan test site. Effective as the wheeling and dealing to set up the deal might have been, much of what Bull did smacks of the amateur and the romantic. Good security is unobtrusive and does not make the thing it is guarding obvious. In the real world, private armies stand out like sore thumbs, and it was not long before Antiguans would be making mocking references to the sealed-off test site. Cab drivers, when pointing out the high mesh fences bisecting the peninsula, told gullible tourists that it was "the lair of Dr. No," referring to the fictional Caribbean island of Crab Key, which was the base of the villain in a James Bond movie.

In 1974, another incident was to further tarnish Bull's reputation in the islands—his strange choice of a doctor for the Barbados facilities. The incident has been portrayed as a case of helping out the friend of a friend; it can also be seen as a sign of some profound change in Bull's hitherto-liberal attitudes.

Still alive and still living in Vienna at the age of ninety-three, Dr. Hermann Erben is, by all accounts, a strange and compelling personality, whose career must be regarded as one of the twentieth century's more bizarre tales. To begin with, he was the best friend of Errol Flynn, the famous movie actor of the 1930s and '40s. He was also a brilliant specialist in tropical diseases, who had made many important discoveries that saved thousands of lives. In the quest for this knowledge, he spent much of the 1920s and '30s working in leper colonies, in remote places like the Solomon Islands.

Yet the young Dr. Erben was no Albert Schweitzer. Besides being a drug smuggler, he was also a virulent anti-Semite, who had joined the Nazi party in 1922. His sojourns in the jungles of the Far East were often a way to avoid prosecution for his activities on behalf of Hitler, during his rise to power. Among other acts, Erben helped plan the assassination of Austrian Chancellor Dollfuss, during a botched Nazi takeover attempt in 1934.

During one of his overseas excursions, Erben established residence in the United States, and became an American citizen in 1930. It was an allegiance he was to repeatedly betray during the course of World War II. Erben became a Gestapo agent, and spied in the U.S., South America and Southeast Asia. At the conflict's end, he was in Shanghai where the dread *Kempai Tai*, the Japanese secret police, used him as an informer in their prisoner of war camps.

Narrowly escaping a trial for treason by American military authorities, in the chaos of post-war China, Erben made his way back to Austria, with the financial aid of his friend, Errol Flynn. But the alternating drives between humanitarian work and fiendish plotting were not stilled. In the next two decades, he worked as a pioneering doctor and free-lance spy in nations like Iran, Saudi Arabia, and Indonesia. On March 21, 1973, the Austrian government awarded him the Golden Cross, one of the nation's highest civilian awards, for his medical work in Afghanistan.

Yet, coincident with the granting of that honor, the good doctor was being tried in a Vienna court for gross negligence in the death of a patient. Found guilty, Dr. Erben was sentenced to three months in prison. The punishment was commuted to a form of house arrest, and the lifting of his medical license for the duration.

While he waited out his sentence, Erben considered the future. As during his previous "embarrassments," he decided it was time to leave Austria for a while.

Despite—some might say because of—his past, Erben knew many members of Austria's political and economic elite, and was an accepted member of Viennese society. At a party in the late 1950s, he was introduced to Sterling Cole, during Cole's tenure as chairman of the Vienna-based International Atomic Energy Commission. The two men soon became fast friends, and the association continued long after Cole became a director of SRC.

Through Cole's good offices, he got Gerry Bull to hire him as the medical officer for the Barbados test site. The seventy-seven-year-old ex-spy held that position from November 1974 to July of 1975. Erben would later boast to *Profil* that the position was "well-paid, but without much effort. We employed many people in Barbados, but they were not sick."

While Bull might be excused a lack of knowledge of Erben's past, Cole certainly could not. Erben was permanently banned from the United States by the Department of Justice, for his war record. Cole had put him touch with U.S. Senator Louis Wyman, who had unsuccessfully lobbied to have the ban on him lifted, in 1968. Yet he recommended that a man declared a security risk and a traitor be hired by a company that did highly classified work for the U.S. government.

What made it more curious was that Erben was often less than discreet about his personal history, and his political views had changed little since the day, shortly before Pearl Harbor, when he stood on the deck of an American ship and gave the Hitler salute as a German vessel, flying the swastika, sailed by. Rumors about Erben, his past, and the racist comments he made, were circulating on the island long before he left. A few short years later, they would be remembered.

While he was there, this strange, magnetic man struck up a kindly-uncle type of friendship with Bull's oldest son, Philippe. The blond-haired, twenty-year-old student, who showed signs of the same mercurial brilliance that his father possessed, was going through a period of emotional stress. Though he had begun university studies in Montréal when he was seventeen, his third-year marks in biological studies were mediocre, and he seemed to lack ambition or purpose.

At least, according to Dr. Erben, that was Gerry Bull's opinion, in the summer of 1975. While back in Austria, on what he described as his "summer vacation," he received an urgent Telex from Bull, through the Vienna offices of Shoul Eisenberg. Gerry wanted him to come to Montréal for an urgent talk, and a ticket and expense money were provided.

In SRC's Montréal offices, a scene was played out that was an echo of Bull's own experience as a young student, when the LaBrosses used their influence to get him into Regiopolis and, later, the University of Toronto. Erben was asked to take Philippe under his wing, and to aid in having him admitted to Vienna's school of medicine. More, he was requested to personally oversee Philippe's studies, a task Erben said he, "was well paid for, of course."

According to *Profil*, when Philippe arrived in Vienna, the young Canadian was at first rejected by the medical academy, because he had not completed the necessary pre-med studies. Erben knew what to do. He instructed Philippe to apply again, and make his biology courses in Montréal appear to be medically related. In addition, he got Shoul Eisenberg to speak to Austria's Chancellor Kriesky on his behalf. Suddenly, all the difficulties disappeared, and Philippe was admitted to the academy. Four years later, he would graduate as a Doctor of Medicine.

When *Profil* queried the retired Kriesky about the incident, in 1985, he didn't remember ever having spoken up personally for Philippe Bull, or having had any communication from Eisenberg. "It could be that Sterling Cole had written to me that he was interested in the son of Bull, but I had forwarded that letter without any comment on my part."

Both Philippe Bull and Erben insisted that it was Eisenberg, not Cole, who approached the Chancellor. But, by 1985, Eisenberg had been in just too many scandals for anyone in Austria to want to admit to any dealings with him, at all. It is more likely that Gerry Bull pulled out all the stops, and both men lobbied the Chancellor on his son's behalf.

Whichever way it went, it was not to be the last time Bull used the influence of his new friends in Austria.

Back in Canada, the operations of SRC were facing a growing financial crisis, by 1975. The fat research contracts of the past decade had vanished. The trickle of work it continued to get from the U.S. and Canadian military, while helpful, was not nearly enough to keep the concern going. Even the Israeli orders, though they kept the cash-flow up, were like blood transfusions; they helped the patient survive, but they could not provide a cure.

Money input was so low Bull that resorted to a tactic common with business managers who have good nerves and a buccaneering streak—screwing the bank. It was easier to do than might be expected. To pay the costs of producing the Israeli shells in the Scranton Arsenal, the First Pennsylvania Bank, America's oldest financial institution, and the nation's twentieth-largest bank, had lent Bull $12 million on the initial order, and $2.2 million on the final batch. Under the chairmanship of John Bunting, its chief executive officer at the time, the bank was trying to shed its traditional image and mediocre profit margins, by getting into the riskier, higher-return field of venture-capital investment.

First Pennyslvania had come up with a new concept it called a "term loan." Under Bunting's scheme, the recipient company's assets were pledged to the bank, and all major management decisions were supposed to be approved by the lender. In return, the bank got an ongoing cut of the firm's activities, which could potentially make it millions.

It was a nice theory that seemed to minimize risk and maximize profits, but it failed to take into account that companies seeking venture capital are usually small and without much in the way of assets. Their real capital is brain-power and ideas. In the case of SRC, eight thousand acres of bush, a few small buildings, and a handful of patents that their own developer could not put to profitable use, were not worth $12 million.

Edward Treon was SRC's treasurer at the time. He was soon to leave the company in frustration and bafflement at Gerry Bull's handling of financial affairs. "You had to feel sorry for the guy," a company insider would later say. "He could not understand Gerry's view of accounting at all."

Treon would later describe the bank's dilemma, to *The Burlington Free Press*, as "having no recourse but to go along and hope...they were hooked."

As the money rolled in from IMI, Bull, instead of paying off the initial debt, used it to meet payrolls and other operational expenses. All the bank got was some initial interest payments and excuses. That their executives were realizing this, is shown by the considerably tighter arrangements on the $2.2 million loan. The agreement was set up so that certain payments went directly into Bull's accounts at the bank, where the funds were immediately sequestered by the loan department. All parties held on to the somewhat Micawberish hope that future business would materialize to cover the shortfalls.

Just what that business might consist of was the major question. Selling the GC-45 and the aeroballistic shell seemed the best bet, but the one thing Bull had learned from the Israeli experience was the vital necessity of having his own independent manufacturing capability. He did not want to be forced to "sell ten-dollar bills for five bucks" again. With single-minded dedication, he set out to acquire every technology needed to manufacture guns, shells, fuses, propellants, and explosives. Financially strapped as SRC might have been in 1975, Bull was able to spend several million dollars, setting up a high-volume shell-machining complex on the Canadian side of Highwater. It was his first step to achieving the full spectrum of artillery capability.

How realistic was the idea? An SRC executive, who joined the company shortly after the decision to attempt it was taken, greeted the question with a wry laugh. "Nothing Gerry ever did appeared realistic, it was always nearly impossible...he was doing it because he thought that he would be able to set up something that would be able to service Canadian government requirements.

"The first part, the shell-machining and production capability, that was realistic. The trouble was...he wanted to do everything. He wanted to do gun barrels. That's where it became less realistic. He even wanted to do forging; in fact, there's a huge building still out there at Highwater—some might call it a white elephant— which was going to be the forging plant."

Like just about everyone who ever worked with Bull, the man was struck by the extraordinary effect he had on people. "One of the things I remember him by is his ability to get you to do things, his charisma. There was no such thing as impossible. You'd walk into his office and, if he told you we can go to the moon, you'd say, 'Yeah, we could probably go to the moon, no big deal.' And then you'd walk out of his office and realize, 'Holy shit, what the hell did we get into?' I can't honestly think of anything I disliked about him, except the hours he kept and the hours we had to keep."

One thing had not changed about Gerry Bull; he still demanded maximum effort of the people he worked with. As the executive recalls, "When I joined SRC, I was about to get married around Christmas time. And he told me, 'Well, you're already married,' and I didn't understand what he said. He repeated it. 'You're married to the company.' And its true, everybody was married to the company.

"Now, lots of businessmen have said things like that. What they really mean is that is you're a slave of the company. But Gerry wasn't made like that. I remember we were in Austria, and he was negotiating the sale of the license for the GC-45 (To Voist-Alpine, in 1979). We were all drunk, everybody got quite pissed. I went to the can, and he came in and stood beside me, and he said, 'We finally got enough money to pay the people back home.' It made me realize that this guy had a human side, he was really worried about all these guys at home.

"The idea of loyalty was very important to him. But the funny thing is, from my experience, the demand was not out of him personally, but it was a demand for the project. In other words, we're going to do something nobody ever did before. When you tell people you're going to do something really amazing, they work a lot, and they work more as a team. In other words, if you just give an average job to a bunch of people, they'll do an average job. When you ask them to do much more than average, they'll do much more than average—that was SRC."

Practical people had said Bull's concept of loyalty to his employees was one of the things that brought him down, in the end. A practical person would have cut staff, and maybe saved the firm. But Bull had an almost-Japanese belief that the boss had an obligation to those, who, more than working for him, he considered *colleagues* in a scientific adventure. The demise of HARP had forced him to lay people off, and he had hated the experience. A stubborn refusal to do it again was coupled with ever-hardening attitudes toward an outside world that always seemed to be thwarting him.

Considering the type of people he was hanging around with in Brussels, it is easy to paint Bull as a man who had grown increasingly cynical and amoral, with the passage of years. While there is some truth in the picture, it might also be said that his ideals had merely narrowed. Their focus was no longer the larger community of a Canadian nation that the LaBrosses had raised him to respect and serve—neither was it the American republic he had taken an oath to— it was just his dreams of space travel, big guns, and the people who supported his visions.

The man who aided Bull in perfecting the GC-45 system, and then helped him sell it, may have come the closest to defining what all the sharks in Brussels, the bland bankers, and the cold-eyed men in Washington, were really dealing with, in 1975.

"Gerry was a salesman. He could sell anything, he could sell you the moon. But he was not necessarily a businessman. That means that he didn't necessarily get the best deal. That's the trouble with all those people who are reading everything about him in the newspapers—all the greed-and-lust stuff—its just not him. He told me once, 'I read the numbers, but I won't be a slave to them.' He wasn't looking at profit. The people around him were talking about that, but I think he was a man who was looking at accomplishing things; whether it was putting something into orbit, or the longest range, or the best gun, whatever it took."

Whatever it took. Damn the rules, and damn the petty people who enforced them. Rebellion against authority and regulation had always been Bull's trademark. Now, as his outlook narrowed, the field he could apply that attitude to grew ever larger. The young professor, who had turned down high pay to stay in Canada, was now forty-eight. He was growing old in a way his younger self could never have understood.

Both Canada and the United States claim patronage of the mighty cannon that was to play such a dramatic role in Bull's career. American sources and investigative reports consistently refer to "American technology" and "U.S. design," in describing the weapon. And why not? Its first barrels were produced in the U.S. army's Watervliet Arsenal in upstate New York; the first test beds rode on old M-114 gun carriages, provided by the American government; and the first shells for it were forged in Scranton.

The Canadian claim is less obvious but, in the end, more persuasive. One does not even have to use the fact of Bull being a native son, with a long career in Canadian military affairs, to make the case.

Michael Bull, in his 1987 interview with Dyllon Roach, denied there was ever any Canadian government assistance to SRC on the project. He said, "SRC never, repeat never, used Canadian tax money to develop the prototype of the GC-45, which is only a conversion of the M-114 gun."

That is true only in the narrowest sense. Canada financed many of the technological steps required to develop the weapon's shell. The DND records, from 1972 to 1978, show a stream of minor contracts to develop and test shell-driving bands, riding nubs, and projectile forebodies. All clearly state that the work is related to SRC's 155mm aeroballistic shell. More than that, Canada funded range trials of both shell and barrel in Gagetown, New Brunswick, and other army ranges in Québec and the West. They also, as seen by the contract to SRC-International, aided in promoting it abroad.

Retired Colonel Brian MacDonald is an artillery specialist, and a former executive director of the Canadian Institute of Strategic Studies. The nature of his duties at the time made him familiar with the test reports of the firing of Bull's shells at the Camp Gagetown ranges as early as 1972. He said, "I never thought it was anything but a Canadian development the army was testing. I know the government believed it was Canadian."

Another retired Canadian army officer had a more direct role in assessing Bull's cannon. In the late '70s, he was with the Directorate of Land Requirements.(DRL) He described his job and the main purpose of DRL as, "trying to buy the guns and ammo the army needed." The officer was intimately involved in the selection process for new ordnance, including the one that subsequently led to Canada's purchase of the American-built M109 155mm Self Propelled (SP) gun. "That project trialed a variety of guns...Bull's proposals [for barrel designs] were not a serious contender at the time, because they were in a low state of development...Later, there was definite interest in his barrels."

He also mentioned that Bull had made a radical proposal for a self-propelled version of the weapon. Unlike all previous Western SP guns, which are track-mounted, his proposal was on wheels—six huge, 21 X 25 tires of a type used on 1950s-era, Canadian-made, heavy earth-moving equipment and mobile crane-carrier chassis. Cheaper and more reliable than track-based systems, this 9.4-meter vehicle would have moved the gun over rough terrain and bad roads at speeds up to ninety kilometers per hour.

The officer stressed that "Bull's technological breakthroughs" were well appreciated by the army's technical staffs. Asked why Canada did not pick up on it, he replied heatedly, "Simple incompetence in gathering together the industrial end, the army's requirements and the available technology. People talk about a military-industrial complex...that implies both of them working efficiently together. In that sense, there's never been one in Canada. Neither in DND, or over in Industry, Trade and Commerce was there the will or the appreciation of the importance of having a coherent national program to retain vital technologies."

In conclusion, he touched on a question that was to come up again and again, in any discussion of the prospects for the GC-45 in the 1970s. "We knew the capabilities of Bull's technologies...they were demonstratably superior. Our only worry was 'Can this be brought into production?'"

Canada has a wide variety of programs and agencies to support its businesses in selling abroad. While companies producing and exporting military equipment must deal with a different web of bureaucracy to get approval for such sales, the financial assistance from the government involves a process that treats the exporter of weaponry no differently than one selling video toys. Its prime thrust is to boost Canadian exports, not make moral or strategic judgments on the utility of such sales.

One organization that provides such aid is the Canadian Commercial Corporation (CCC). A Crown corporation, currently responsible to the Federal Minister for International Trade, it will assume the role of prime contractor in an export deal. Not only will it arrange loans for an exporter to produce the product involved, CCC also guarantees the purchaser (often a foreign government) that the order will be produced, whatever happens to the company doing it.

This means that CCC sometimes ends up with the responsibility for reorganizing companies that are in dire financial straits, or have actually gone bankrupt. While CCC attempts to have the work completed in Canada, using the original firm's facilities, it will find another company to finish the job, if necessary. If a Canadian concern cannot be found to do the work, it will go to foreign sources to complete the deal.

Shefford Electronics was such a company. Michael Bull describes it as "an entity which we purchased, in 1975, in Granby, Québec. It was bankrupt, and it was purchased at the urging of the government. Its product was radio direction-finding equipment. They had a contract with Nigeria, when we purchased it through the CCC. The company was going belly-up, and that really embarrassed the hell out of CCC, because they were legally liable for it. So they were after us to buy it, and we did."

Michael was only nineteen at the time these events occurred, and was not involved in his father's business affairs. Still a student, he had given up on biology and transferred to Québec City's Laval University, where he took business administration and accountancy in French. Fluently bilingual, he has a tendency to speak of events in the plural, when talking of his father's earlier days. It reflects a passionate commitment to his father's memory and reputation in particular, and that of the Bull family in general.

"My father was an extremely impatient man. Had he had somebody with a little bit more restraint around him at the time, they would have said, 'Wait, we'll put in conditions, subject to the securing of grants from the government.' But he jumped in, like was his habit, then we asked for the grants, the regular grants. They said, 'Well, give us some *pro formas* on the company.' My father was a very optimistic person, so he made the *pro formas* on that basis, and they came back and said, 'Well, you're too rich, you're going to make a profit within two years, you don't need a subsidy.' Then he said, 'What do we have to do?' They said, 'Well, with those projections, you can't get it.' So we redid the projections on a more conservative basis, and then they said we were too poor. It went on and on and on.

"The bulk of it is, we managed to finish at loss, at our loss, the Nigerian contract. We had cost overruns [but] keeping in mind that it was a very new product, it was all right—if things had gone better in the future."

Michael does not mention another reason his father had for jumping into the purchase. Shefford was Canada's major producer of fuses for 155mm artillery shells.

That same year, Gerry Bull reorganized his business activities, and continued to expand their scope. A holding company, Canadian Technical Industries (CTI), was formed with Mimi Bull, who was the major shareholder. Based in Montréal, it can be seen as a line of defense against the First Pennsylvania Bank, which was getting increasingly worried about Bull's activities (At one point, First Pennsylvania was loaning SRC Vermont $100,000 a month, so Bull could pay the interest on the original loans!). Threats of foreclosure on the Highwater facilities, with their immediate corollary of bankruptcy for Bull's operations, were becoming more vehement.

Yet Bull kept buying things. By 1977, CTI's holdings not only included SRC-Q, SRC-Vermont, and Shefford, but Forge de l'Est (the nominal owner of the never-completed forging complex at Highwater) and a munitions plant near Valleyfield, Québec.

Founded as a government-owned factory during World War II, the plant produced propellants for guns, and the high explosives for their shells. Fronting on the south shore of the St. Lawrence River, twenty-five miles southwest of Montréal, the thousand-acre facility was criss-crossed by a twenty-four-mile-long network of roads and railways. Comprising some two hundred buildings, storage bunkers, and chemical tanks, the operation was widely dispersed for obvious safety reasons.

Closed and re-opened several times in the post-war era, the installation was privatized in 1965, as Canadian Arsenals Ltd., and sold to Canadian Industries Ltd.(CIL) They expanded the product range to include the manufacture of TNT. Almost totally dependent on erratic army orders for explosives, the plant's operations were maintained at what a statement by the present owners calls "varying levels of intensity between 1965 and 1977." In fact, business was so bad that the staff had been reduced to 250 people, and the plant to virtual caretaker status.

Sick of carrying the losses, CIL informed the government that it would close the facility, if a buyer could not be found. Since Canadian Arsenals was the last indigenous producer of military explosives in Canada, the government went looking for a buyer who would purchase what seemed to be a guaranteed money-loser.

In late 1977, CIL sold the plant to Valleyfield Chemical Products Corporation, and the facility became known by that name. Valleyfield Chemical Products was a wholly-owned subsidiary of CTI.

Michael Bull represents it as another example of his father being taken in. Asked if the purchase was truly not his father's idea, he responded, "Definitely. I'm trying to find some stronger words; they urged it, demanded it. Yes, they helped arrange the financing. They did, and by doing that, they nailed the last nail in our coffin."

The government was so eager to have Bull take over the plant that they provided the new company with over $11 million in grants, to modernize the facilities. Strangely, however, it was this basket-case company that turned out to be potentially the brightest star in the CTI holdings.

Jean Vezena, the man Bull hired to run the new firm, has been described as "very sharp...unflappable...an excellent executive."

Reorganizing the moribund operations, he quickly established efficient production methods, with the enthusiastic cooperation of the local staff members, who had been despairing of their jobs. Moreover, knowing the government's desire to keep the plant open, he hardballed them in negotiations, and forced DND to regularize its powder-purchasing procedures, so the company had a stable base of orders at realistic (read profitable) prices.

Not at all overwhelmed by Bull's charisma, Vezena felt it was his responsibility to run Valleyfield on a businesslike basis, and turn a profit for its owners. He accomplished this by keeping Gerry Bull from meddling in day-to-day operations. Unfortunately, when it later came to more strategic decisions, he either was unable to dissuade Bull, or else simply went along with what looked like a profitable scam.

Corporate diversification was not the only tack Bull took, to try and get his operations on an even keel. Under Bill Friend, a training-munitions development program was established. Low-cost sub-calibre rounds, for tanks and artillery, were produced and sold to the Canadian army.

Parallel to that, Bull's electronics specialists, on the Vermont side of the Highwater compound, had come up with an interesting civilian product—radar-display simulators for training air traffic controllers. One multi-screen installation was promptly sold to the Canadian Department of Transport for use at Montréal's Dorval airport, and the company believed it had found a profitable niche. For overseas sales, Bull signed a marketing agreement with Aircraft Equipment International. This British firm became SRC's exclusive agent for Jordan, Egypt and South Africa. The latter nation was also quick to place an order.

As useful and promising as these activities were, they could not provide an answer to Bull's financial problems. Selling the GC-45, which insured at least one large initial order of shells, was the only answer SRC and its creditors could see. To do that required customers, and it was to the Brussels arms bazaar that Bull once more turned to find them.

Thailand was a nation that could have easily turned to the United States, to fulfil its needs for new artillery pieces to equip the Royal Thai Marines. But Thailand is the only nation in Asia, besides Japan, to have escaped the travail of European colonialism. Shrewdly, it has developed a tradition of not tying itself too tightly to anyone. It was this independent streak that led them to look at European artillery systems, and brought them to the offices of Jacques Heymans sometime in early 1978.

The Thais were impressed with the GC-45, even though it only existed in prototype form. After initial meetings with Bull in Brussels, and subsequent visits to Highwater, their mission returned home, where the proposal was under consideration for over a year. In the spring of 1977, they finally placed an order, worth between $8 million and $12 million, for a dozen guns.

The Canadian Ministry of External Affairs had no problem with the sale. Thailand was a friendly nation that was known as an ally of the West. CCC was more than willing to assist SRC, a company it was already doing business with. Not only did it help SRC get loans to produce the weapons, it provided the Thai government with performance guarantees.

Later, it would not seem a prudent move, considering the rumors and news stories that were beginning to surface about SRC at the time. Were they really unaware that Gerry Bull had found another customer for his mighty gun?

CHAPTER 11

One of the more curious ironies of Gerry Bull's life is that he will probably be remembered longest in a country he never visited— Angola. More than one Canadian visitor to that sad and war-torn land has been surprised to hear his name mentioned, when their place of origin becomes known. From illiterate peasants near the Namibian border to humorless government bureaucrats in the capital of Luanda, they all know about Canada and Gerry Bull. "Ah, yes," they say, "the man with the big gun."

As the winds of change blew through Africa in the 1950s, the Portuguese colonies there seemed islands of tranquility in a continent that was beginning to shake from the forces of nationalism and liberation. Unlike colonial powers with democratic governments back home, which had inadvertently infected their colonial subjects with dangerous ideas of self-rule, the Portugal ruled by the crypto-fascist dictator, Oliveira Salazar, thought that Angola, Guinea-Bissau and Mozambique were "a special case."

As the 1960s began in Angola, they found out just how mistaken they were. After attempts at peaceful dialogue with their occupiers were answered by massacre and imprisonment, three resistance movements, the FNLA, the MPLA and UNITA, began fighting a classic guerrilla war. Largely based on tribal groupings, they adopted Marxist and Maoist ideologies, more for their military doctrines and the access to weaponry than for the effectiveness of their politics.

While America was fixated by the Vietnam war, the struggle in Angola escalated, throughout the 1960s, until it was the world's second-largest conflict. Out of sight of the world's TV cameras, terrorist raids on colonial farmers were answered by the napalming of native villages, and a wave of murder unleashed by PIDE, the Portuguese secret police.

Backed by several billion dollars' worth of American arms, Portugal sent a half-million poorly paid and worse led draftees into a meat grinder that seemingly had no end. But, when the end did come, the source was totally unexpected, by government and rebels alike. The professional officer corps of the Portuguese army, vastly inflated by a wave of unwilling university graduates, was more open to new thoughts than most segments of Portuguese society. Only they were allowed to read "subversive, communist propaganda," for the purpose of better understanding the enemy's military tactics.

Disgusted with the corruption that sapped the army's strength and killed its young soldiers, many officers, including some generals, came to compare the Angolans' situation with the one their own people faced at home, and it radicalized them. Slowly, in ever-larger groups, they began to talk, and then to plot. The result was the 1974 military coup, which overthrew the dictatorship and eventually led to a democratic Portuguese government.

The first act of the rebel officers was to declare a unilateral cease-fire in the colonial wars and precipitously evacuate their army, not only from Angola, but from their other embattled colonies of Guinea-Bissau and Mozambique. Several hundred thousand Portuguese civilians followed them, taking, in the words of one observer, "everything they could carry, be it maps of the telephone system or typewriters from government offices."

In the chaos that remained behind, the uneasy alliance of the insurgent groups splintered, and they began to fight for control of the new nation. Faced with the need for outside support, some odd, and not so odd, relationships were established. South Africa and the United States began aiding the FNLA and, to a lesser extent, UNITA, which had also received aid from communist China and was then espousing a Maoist political doctrine.

The largest, and most successful, group, the MPLA, which had borne the brunt of the struggle against the Portuguese, reaffirmed its long-standing relationship with the Soviet Union. In 1975, in the greatest military strategic airlift in history, the USSR flew over a hundred thousand tons of weaponry to Angola. Along with a horde of East-bloc advisors, came Cuban artillery units and support personnel.

While the FNLA drowned and disappeared in this wave of steel—many of its fighters defecting to the new MPLA government—UNITA proved a tougher nut to crack. Led by the charismatic Dr. Jonas Samvimbi, it was—and still is—based in the remote Ovumbu lands of southern Angola.

To understand why UNITA was not destroyed, one need only look at the terrain in which it was spawned. Down by the Namibian border, in a region the Portuguese called the *Fin du Mundo*—the end of the world—is a quarter-million square kilometers of low, rolling hills and harsh, scrub brush. Always hot, and by seasonal turns parched or stiflingly humid, it is a place of great extremes and little succor for man or beast. As one traveller put it, "You can drown in it one month, and die of thirst the next."

A dozen guerrilla armies could hide in its vastness and never be brought to battle and, in the 1970s and early 1980s, that scenario was almost literally true. MPLA, UNITA, SWAPO, ZAPU, ZANU—all these African liberation forces fought, trained and died in the *Fin du Mundo* at some time in that bloody period.

In a 1976 book, entitled *Southern Africa: The New Politics of Revolution*, Joe Slovo, head of the South African Communist Party and of the African National Congress's military wing, *Umkhonto we Sizwe* (Spear of the Nation), gave this analysis of South Africa's reaction to events. "...the Lisbon coup and Portugal's withdrawal from Angola and Mozambique have altered the strategic balance in southern Africa by removing two of the lesser props to white rule and rendering a third, Rhodesia, much less viable as a buffer state."

While South Africa saw itself being surrounded by a ring of self-proclaimed "front-line states," the United States viewed events in Angola from a cold-war perspective. That the Soviet Union was doing the same thing did not help matters. In Washington, it was decided that American reaction to the Russian airlift and "the Kremlin's new janissaries in Africa" (Cuban combat forces) must be a strong one.

Through the C.I.A., the United States provided funding and military equipment to UNITA and the FNLA, via Zambia and South Africa itself. That they backed a loser in the FNLA, and a non-winner with Savimbi's UNITA, put paid to their attempts to defeat the Russian-supplied MPLA forces and install a government "more supportive of Western interests." That they had cooperated with the ultimate, long-term loser in the region—Afrikaner racial and military "superiority"—did not seem apparent at the time.

Yet the facts were there from the beginning. In 1975, the South African Defence Forces (SADF) launched a major offensive into Angola, from what was then their colony of Namibia. It was a last-ditch attempt to rescue the fading fortunes of the FNLA. While they penetrated over four hundred miles, and came within a four-hour drive of the Angolan capital of Luanda, the mission was a failure, and very nearly a complete disaster for the forces involved.

All had gone well, at first. Equipped with French and U.S. tanks, and supported by Mirage jet fighter-bombers, the five thousand-man SADF force had a two thousand-man white mercenary group fighting alongside it. Paid for and recruited by the C.I.A. in Britain, the U.S., France, Germany, Portugal and Zaire, these men were to prove better at shooting civilians than at standing the stern tests of combat.

Blowing away the ragtag MPLA military units that stood in their way, the attack force blitzkrieged north and linked up with FNLA troops, for a final drive on Luanda. As the columns passed beyond range of their air cover, Cuban artillery observers in the hills ahead began registering targets. From as far as twenty-five kilometers behind them, massed batteries of Soviet guns and 122mm rocket launchers rained thousands of shells on the stranded columns, forcing them to spread out and seek cover.

Correctly judging the FNLA and mercenary troops to be the weak part of the force, the Soviet military advisors, who now commanded the Angolan government forces, made them the target of a counteroffensive. Newly equipped and well trained MPLA infantry battalions, with Cuban advisors, launched sudden attacks supported by heavy artillery barrages. The FNLA troops either scattered into the bush or surrendered in droves.

The "crack mercenary force" fared no better. Finding that their South African-provided Panhard armored cars were deathtraps in the face of Soviet RPG-7 bazookas, they panicked. Frantic efforts by their commanders to restore order by summary executions only led to more disorder. Those who were not killed or captured, either fled northeast into Zaire, or managed to attach themselves to retreating South African columns.

With their allies destroyed, and an invisible wall of guns in front of them, the South African adventure, and any hope of a "friendly" government in Luanda, was over. Yet, even as they backpeddled for the Namibian border, the cause of the debacle was being studied in Pretoria.

It wasn't that hard to figure out. Like a chain, armies are only as strong as the weakest of their components, and South Africa's major deficiency was artillery. Its old, British, World War II, 5.5-inch howitzers and 25-pounder field guns were inadequate, both in quantity and quality, when it came to opposing the Soviet guns and rocket launchers deployed in Angola.

With words like "vital to the survival of the nation," the SADF high command told the government that the problem must be resolved.

In light of fading American support, and what they saw as the perfidy and weakness of European nations, the government decided the solution must be a South African one.

In 1976, the South African government issued a specification for a new and revolutionary cannon, to meet the challenge of Soviet long-range guns. But where to find such a weapon, and how to make it at home? There was nothing in the American or European arsenals that could meet the requirement, and South Africa lacked the machinery, and the technical staffs required for both artillery-shell and barrel production.

William Stockwell was a member of the C.I.A.'s Angola task force until he resigned from the agency in 1977, ostensibly in disagreement with American policy in Africa. In an interview, aired on November 7, 1978, by the Canadian Broadcasting Corporation's current-affairs program, *the fifth estate*, he said, "At one time, we wanted to send 155mm ammunition to South Africa. They had requested it, and we wanted to honor the request. We also wanted to send some additional arms to our allies inside Angola. The concept was to send a ship with ammunition to Windhoek, South West Africa. The South Africans would distribute this ammunition and material into Angola, [but] the 155 ammunition would have been for their own 155 tubes: not in Angola, they were in South Africa. We were stopped from doing this by Ambassador Mulcahy of the State Department.

"We were frustrated in that plan, and we did not develop another plan to ship ammunition or material to South Africa. However, the C.I.A. didn't change its stance of being willing to cooperate with South Africa; we just weren't permitted to do it then."

Coming from a critic who apparently had caused the agency "a great deal of embarrassment," it seems a reasonable statement. But a harder look leaves one wondering where Mr. Stockwell really stood.

The first thing an apprentice stage-magician learns is the value of distraction in presenting illusions, and so it is in the world of intelligence. While some dismiss the word, *disinformation*, as just a fancy term for *lie*, it is much more than that. The highest form of the art uses truth to cover reality.

A thorough search of press reports and defense publications, such as *Jane's* and *MILITARY TECHNOLOGY's World Military Balance*, reveals an odd fact. There is not one mention that South Africa ever had a 155mm artillery piece previous to its 1979 announcement of indigenous production of the G-5 155mm gun. Even if it had been able to scrounge a few old ones in the global arms market, the numbers could not have been significant.

The idea that the inadvertently-discovered shell transfers to South Africa could be turned around, and used as a cover for what was really going on, might seem far-fetched, but that was exactly what happened—the media saw the shells, and turned the references about "several gun barrels" into footnotes.

Why would South Africa need shells from Canada and the United States, if they were building their own guns? The answer lies in the nature of the three components that make up an artillery system; tubes, shells and explosives.

From a manufacturing point of view, the tube is actually the easiest thing to produce, because one does not need to make that many of them. While it requires special milling machines and high-strength steels, South Africa's mineral wealth gave it a solid base of metallurgical technologies, and access to many Western nations with the necessary machine tools.

Explosives are the next level of difficulty, since the knowledge base and processing machinery, for safe production of large volumes of propellant and warhead charges, are both complex and costly.

The simplest part of the system, the empty shell, is the kicker. To produce a usable round, three industrial steps are required—rough forging, machining and filling. Step three is both obvious and the easiest. However, steps one and two require mass-production facilities to turn out the thousands of rounds a day that any army in combat will need. It is the time needed to construct such facilities, especially the forging plant, that would have slowed the South Africans down the most. Any new artillery piece requires mass firings of prototypes, to proof both weapon and shell, so that any faults can be corrected before full production begins. Wear rates, ballistics, and many other factors can only be tested in this way.

Remember that Stockwell said, "At one time we wanted to send 155mm ammunition to South Africa...the 155 ammunition would have been for their own 155 tubes: not in Angola, they were in South Africa."

At the remote Schmidtsdrift proving ground, 250 miles southwest of Johannesburg in the wilds of Betchuanaland, near the fabled Kimberley diamond mines, South Africa was firing thousands of shells, to test and refine its newfound answer to the Soviet long-range rocket and artillery systems. It was a long-barrelled howitzer of unprecedented range, accuracy and terminal destructive effect, for which they would produce the tubes, shells and powder in near-record time.

Commandant Piet Marais, the first head of South Africa's ARM-SCOR, was a simple, direct man. When asked the purpose of his organization, he barked, "To break the [U.N. arms] embargo; to show it up for the pitiful thing it is." Lauded in the local media for nearly three decades, ARMSCOR is still admired by many white South Africans for its pivotal role in maintaining their military supremacy over the rest of the continent. Abroad, its power and importance are generally misunderstood.

Formed in 1964, the same year the United Nations applied military sanctions against South Africa, it was set up as a state-owned corporation. It is, in fact, an executive arm of the government, with wide powers to intervene in all aspects of the South African economy. All weapons research, acquisition and production are coordinated through it. Able to tap the resources of the South African diplomatic and intelligence services, it has masterminded scores of covert purchasing operations in many countries, including Canada.

The plebeian nature of most of its work has been its best cover. As one defense analyst put it, "Who can get excited about a crate of gasket rings?" The transfer of Gerry Bull's mighty GC-45 gun, plus the technology to produce it in South Africa as the G-5, can be taken as an exception.

Just how it started, and who was responsible, will never be known for certain. The cloudiness of the issue is a perfect example of how the world of intelligence-gathering and covert operations really works. In the wilderness of mirrors, superiors make suggestions, and they do not want to know about methods. If anything goes wrong, their asses are covered. Applied to the multiple layers of bureaucracy in the American foreign-policy and intelligence communities, it often means that those held responsible at the higher levels may have no idea of what subordinates, many rungs below them, are really doing.

On March 30, 1982, the Subcommittee on Africa of the Foreign Affairs Committee of the American House of Representatives released its report on the ARMSCOR/SRC affair. According to its staff study, "it is probable that a U.S. defense consultant who was assisting the C.I.A.'s covert action program in Angola, and who was under the supervision of a C.I.A. officer, planned with South African government officials [to provide] shipments of U.S.-origin arms for use in Angola. He also informed the South African representatives of ARMSCOR...that they could obtain superior 155mm artillery from SRC.

"Much of this planning and discussion took place after the U.S. government had decided not to ship arms for Angola via South Africa, and not to respond to an official South African request for 155mm artillery from SRC."

In March of 1981, W5, a Canadian CTV-network current-affairs show, referred to the U.S. refusal with this statement. "The C.I.A. never carried out that plan, a plan which would have been illegal in the U.S.. Did the agency drop the idea altogether, or did it look for an alternative route?"

Then they quoted Mr. Stockwell. "If the C.I.A. wanted to facilitate a deal between a private company and South Africa, they would have to work through the Department of Defense, they would have to pull strings in the State Department...I would think that, for the delivery of arms to South Africa, particularly a sensitive weapon, it would have to be the Assistant Secretary of State for African Affairs, and most likely the Secretary of State would have to know about it."

W5 asked, "Henry Kissinger?"

Stockwell replied, "In that case, yes."

Gerry Bull made an interesting reference to this tale, in 1987. Speaking of the ordeal of his trial in 1980, he said, "I was under a tremendous amount of pressure—all types of pressure. People wanted me to implicate other people to improve my case—people I'm not sure had anything to do with it or not." Who were these people he was supposed to implicate? Bull responded, "Well, Henry Kissinger was one of them."

There is a well-known tendency for intelligence operatives to become partisans of the groups they liaise with. The official refusal to help South Africa resulted in a great deal of anger at the operational level. Their hopes of striking what they saw as a decisive blow against Soviet power in Africa were thwarted. Could a desire to punish their superiors for "abandoning our friends," have been part of the plot?

We know today that the C.I.A. officer the congressional committee referred to was John Clancey III, then a U.S. Marine officer on detachment to the spy agency. Stockwell described him as the epitome of the "good soldier...he was like a pistol...you pointed him in the right direction and pulled the trigger."

The U.S. defense consultant was a retired army lieutenant colonel, John "Jack" Frost, a man whose pictures show a disturbing similarity to another rogue American military man, Oliver North. Even the sunglasses are the same style. Other sources have described him as a freelance arms dealer, a C.I.A. contract man, and "an inveterate hustler, trying to make a fortune."

Brussels is a long way from Angola, but Jack Frost knew the place well. And why not? He had been a "consultant" to PRB, and a business partner of Jacques Heymans, back in the days of the Israeli shell transfer. He knew all about Highwater and Gerry Bull's guns, for he was now a consultant for SRC, as well.

Frost told a tale about the gun transfer to the C.B.C.'s *fifth estate* that is more coherent than Stockwell's, but no less evasive. It is a beautiful example of dissimulation and damage control. "I had a discussion with a Dennis Zeederberg, who then was a member of the [South African] Armaments Board. I told him that, if he had no artillery capability, that the acquisition of Space Research technology was rather useful; that I was willing to undertake a program to see if I could get authorization to transfer the technology." The implication Frost left with *the fifth estate* was that the principals cut him out of the transfer, after he had made the initial connection. "After two months, I was told that South Africa had no interest, because it cost too much money...at that moment, I felt that South Africa had withdrawn from the program."

Not so. In late 1975, a South African ARMSCOR delegation, Zeederberg among them, visited Bull's Highwater site, from the U.S. side of the border in Troy, Vermont. Through his contacts in the intelligence community, Frost says he heard of this trip, and that he got worried he might be blamed for the initial contact on an illegal deal.

"I immediately called to see Dr. Bull, and he did answer the phone, and I asked him if he had been visited, and he admitted he had had a visit from Zeederberg and Beaman, and at that point I said, 'Well, you can't continue this, because it's illegal, and you'd better stop it immediately.' His response was, 'Well, Jack, we don't think we'll do anything, because it looks as if it's too chancy.'

"Now you've got to remember, though, I also had been in this business long enough not to do foolish things, so that I immediately made a report to the Office of Munitions Control, to explain the transaction. And when I made the report, I thought the transaction had been terminated."

The Office of Munitions Control (OMC) is a department of the Bureau of Politico-Military Affairs in the U.S. State Department. They are responsible for the licensing of all American exports of military-related equipment and technology. As such, they played a critical and curious role in the shell exports to South Africa.

The man Frost went to talk with there was Clyde Bryant, Chief of the OMC's Support Services Division. In testifying to the congressional committee, he and his immediate superior, William Robinson, Director of the Bureau of Politico-Military Affairs, had this exchange with Representative Crockett, of Michigan:

MR. CROCKETT
I understand that, in December 1975, during the Angolan war, a U.S. citizen...reported to your agency that he was working with an American official to obtain U.S.-origin arms for South Africa from Thailand and Taiwan. Then he named the U.S. official and the South African government representatives. My question is, did you inquire about the U.S. offical's activity with other agencies, and did you speak to the C.I.A. about it, since they were known to be involved in Angola.

MR. ROBINSON
I have never met Mr. Frost. I have never seen him. He came to my office once, to my knowledge: he talked to Mr. Bryant. It is alleged that he gave us a written

report. He has never given us a written report on anything, to my knowledge, and here again I would suggest; well, he has never given us a written report on anything. I will let Mr. Bryant take it from there.

MR. CROCKETT
Did Mr. Bryant write a report?

MR. ROBINSON
He wrote a memorandum for the record...it was alleged Mr. Frost provided us subsequently with a written report, which he never has.

MR. CROCKETT
Forget that...my question is whether or not there was any follow-up action on what Mr. Frost supposedly told your office.

Robinson did not answer the question, but passed the buck to his subordinate. Bryant denied Frost had mentioned a specific U.S. official, and maintained he had acted properly in merely passing on a brief memorandum of the conversation to the State Department's Bureau of Intelligence and Research, "and a sister office within our own bureau."

MR. CROCKETT
Am I correct that Frost was known to your agency as a Space Research consultant?

MR. BRYANT
I think he may have been on record with our office in that regard, but I was not aware of it, sir, and the record is a very narrow record.

The activities of Frost in facilitating certain aspects of the financial transfers from ARMSCOR to SRC-Québec, would make that record meaningless, and his words a blatant lie.

CHAPTER 12

Much has been written about Bull's connections with the C.I.A.—the appointment of ex-Deputy Director Richard Bissel to be his lobbyist in Washington, the visits of Director Admiral Stanfield Turner and other high-ranking officials to the Highwater site—yet it can be asked what good it really did him. Small companies don't hire high-priced lobbyists to maintain their connections with the U.S. government, they do it in a desperate attempt to gain influence and business. There is no evidence that Bull's "show and tell" tours of his facilities produced anything more than appreciative comments from the leaders of the American intelligence community. They certainly didn't come up with the money he needed to keep SRC afloat. There weren't that many situations in the world where the application of small amounts of advanced artillery-shell technology could help the agency achieve its objectives. Frustrated in his efforts to flog the GC-45 to Canada, the U.S. and other NATO nations, the ARMSCOR offer may have seemed too tempting to pass up, C.I.A.-approved or not.

After the initial denials, when the scam was first unraveling, neither Gerry then, nor Michael Bull now, ever denied the shell shipments to South Africa took place. What they denied was that any wrongdoing was involved, since they claim SRC had the approval of the U.S. government to do it, even if violated the law. It is the "we were acting under orders" defense.

On a moral plane, the responsibility of individuals in such situations has been debated in places as far afield as the Nuremburg war-crimes tribunal and the trial of Colonel Oliver North. Like any ethical question, the issue will never be resolved.

Legally, as the American court system keeps explaining in its judgments on cases such as the Nixon-era Watergate scandal and the Reagan administration's arms-to-Iran case, the argument doesn't wash. Law is law, and guilt is guilt. All a convicted person can do is plead extenuating circumstances, and ask for mercy.

When it comes to the transfer of the GC-45 design into the South African G-5, the Bull's have always strenuously denied any involvement whatsoever. Gerry Bull claimed that "ARMSCOR ripped me off...the G-5 is nothing but a shoddy copy of my weapon." Michael Bull has speculated that South Africa saw the gun at one of the international arms shows, where SRC exhibited, and copied the idea from there. There is a very practical reason for taking this position. To say anything else would be admitting to an illegal act, which neither Bull or SRC was ever formally charged with. Yet, as was shown in the preceding chapter, the shells without the guns to fire them would have been a somewhat pointless exercise.

On the Bull/SRC side, it is certain that the C.I.A. did have a covert policy of aiding South Africa, in Angola and elsewhere, during the early 1970s, a policy that was later reversed. The question, of course, is when.

On the other hand, the tangled web of political objectives and policy reversals may simply have created a milieu in which Bull could convince government officials, by a nudge and a wink, that he was carrying out a C.I.A.-approved and quasi-legal secret operation, just like the ones they had helped approve for him before.

The major argument for this is the way the operation was financed. Gerry Bull had a hard time coming up with the money to purchase the shell forgings. That hardly seems the hallmark of a C.I.A.-supported operation.

In the congressional testimony, two remarkable letters, which the OMC gave to Gerry Bull, are discussed at length. Bull needed these letters to get final approval on a loan from his major creditor, the First Pennsylvania Bank, to cover the shell purchases. In doing so, he created a paper trail that was to convict him in a court of law.

During the hearings, Howard Wolpe, congressman from Michigan, and Chairman of the Subcommittee on Africa, tried to pin down a pivotal point of the ARMSCOR affair by asking William Robinson, of the

OMC, "Why did OMC indicate, in it's April 8, 1976, letter to SRC, that non-machined, rough-nosed artillery-shell forgings could be exported without a license if they weren't clearly identifiable as arms?"

Mr. Wolpe went on to refer to a second letter from SRC, dated April 21, 1976, in which Bull requested confirmation of his understanding that these blanks would be regarded as non-military items. He demanded to know if "you were under the impression that SRC, when it's officers came to see you, was something other than a munitions exporter or a munitions manufacturer?"

Mr. Robinson replied, "Mr. Chairman, we have about one thousand, eight hundred to two thousand applicants. I worry about a lot of them. The president of a company who has had a long-term contract with the U.S. Department of Defense, accompanied by a distinguished Lieutenant General, retired from the U.S. army, would not be at the top of my hit list."

Doggedly, the chairman came back to the absurdity of classifying an artillery-shell blank as a non-military item. "Maybe there is something that is missing me here, but what is a manufacturer of munitions hardware? He writes to you, in your capacity as a controller of the munitions list and the person who decides whether or not munitions can be exported, he writes to you, and you write back, saying, 'Well, if it's not clearly identifiable as ammunition, then the rough-nosed, non-machined forgings would not be on the list.'"

"Now...they misused it [the letter]. Mr. Bull lied and, as you know, Mr. Bull went to jail." Robinson's answer was an evasion, but what he said was true. Bull's lie was the ultimate destination of the shells. His letters to the OMC said one of the recipients was to be Israeli Military Industries. Another was supposedly SRC International, in Brussels.

Wolpe pressed on, and the long relationship between Bull and the OMC became obvious. "Before these applications, how many times had your office handled applications for export of artillery shells and shell forgings, let's say in the previous five years or so?"

"Mr. Chairman...a search of our records indicates to me that, during the period 1972 to 1975, there were only seven such applications, and they're all from SRC, and you received copies of them."

Wolpe didn't seem to be aware of that. He was shocked. "All were from SRC? All?" he demanded.

When Robinson reiterated the point, the chairman moved on into another murky area of the affair. "...in the same letter [April 21, 1976] to SRC, you indicate the U.S. government had no interest in technologies SRC exported from it's Canadian subsidiary to it's Belgian one. Why did you offer that opinion, without seeing any evidence that the technology was of Canadian, rather than American, origin?... I believe that Mr. Bull, in fact, did raise this question in his April 21 letter...precisely whether or not U.S. approval was needed for the export of technology from a Canadian subsidiary."

Robinson answered, "I believe, if you look at page one, he refers to Canadian-technology export and, as far as we are concerned, any technology of Canadian origin is a matter between the Canadian government and SRC-Québec."

This brought up the critical issue of national ownership of the shell and gun technology. The point being addressed was whether the materials Bull was accused of transferring was, indeed, under U.S. control. It soon became clear that the multi-national, cross-border nature of SRC had confused the State Department. Later, Chairman Wolpe tried to clarify the point with Clyde Bryant, of the OMC. He asked, "Were you under the impression this was a Canadian company?"

In referring to the content of the April 26 letter, Bryant replied, "It would appear that we were dealing with several companies. Not only Space Research in the United States, but Space Research-Québec and a Space Research-International, located in Belgium. Mr. Bull's question centered on the activities of the Canadian firm, over which we would have no control, and on the activities of SRC-I, located in Belgium, over which we would have no control."

"So," Wolpe said, "the problem, from your perspective, is that you were not aware that the technology in question was, in fact, American technology."

"That is correct," Bryant replied.

The chairman went on to state that the "U.S. Customs amassed evidence that the technology was, indeed, American," but one has to ask what that evidence could be. Bull's history, and the way the ERFB round was developed, clearly stamp it as Canadian.

But this did not change the fact that the shells were of American manufacture. The committee also learned that this was not the first time that SRC and the OMC had played fast and loose with the export regulations, with regard to SRC's American-made-shell exports.

Referring to the 1973-74 shipments of 175mm shells by SRC to Israel, Wolpe asked Bryant "Why did your bureau supply SRC with only in-transit licenses for weapons shipments to Canada, to New York, then to Israel, when any weapon on shipment beginning in the U.S. needs a regular export license, as distinguished from an in-transit license?"

Bryant replied with a piece of bafflegab that was not only an evasion, but would reveal just how little knowledge or control the OMC really had over what Bull was doing. "I think the submission of SRC for an application for an in-transit license is evidence, on the part of SRC, that they recognized that this transaction required the approval of the U.S. government."

The shells referred to had left and reentered the United States by crossing a line in the middle of the Highwater compound! It soon became clear that the OMC had not appreciated what it meant to have a factory in two countries at the same time.

Bryant continued his statement with "I am under the impression, your staff can correct me if I am wrong, but it [the in-transit license] referred to projectiles that were produced in a Space Research plant in Québec."

The chairman said no. "The reference is to a U.S. plant."

Bryant responded, "I would have to look at the application, sir."

While the Chairman was correct on what the document said, both men were right, in that the shells were manufactured in two countries. The very ambiguity of Bull's cross-border operations, which had so appealed to the C.I.A. in its previous dealings with him, created a situation that made knowledge of what he was doing difficult, if not impossible, to acquire.

Interviewed for the January, 1983, issue of *MILITARY TECHNOLOGY* magazine, ARMSCOR head Piet Marais described Gerry Bull as "an extremely good technician, but in no way a businessman...this was to cause some trouble later."

The First Pennsylvania Bank would ruefully come to agree with that assessment. To cover the purchase of the forgings from the U.S. government-owned shell plant in Scranton, Pennsylvania, they were scheduled to advance $14.5 million, in the form of guaranteed letters of credit and direct loans, over a ten-month period. However, by May 12, 1976, Bull already owed them $12 million from his previous operations, and couldn't pay it. The bank faced the classic dilemma of any large creditor—the only hope of getting their money back was to loan the debtor more.

But they were nervous. An internal bank memorandum on the new loan referred to "SRC's dubious ability, based on past experience, to estimate costs, produce profits, and the lack of any independent productive capacity." Not only did the bank demand assurances, in the form of the OMC letters, it forced Bull to put up all his U.S.-held patents as additional security.

Bull's tendency to go over budget, indeed to resolutely ignore financial reality, showed up often in SRC's operations. One prime example is the running costs of the Antigua test site. Part of the agreement with Bird's government was the celebrated Antiguan Defence Force, which SRC undertook to train, pay and equip. Even in the Caribbean, three-hundred-man private armies don't come cheaply. Maintaining this force was a severe drain on SRC finances.

In March of 1976, according to the congressional investigation's final report, representatives of Paragon Holdings, a Barbados-based SRC subsidiary, met with officers of Colet Trading Establishment of Liechtenstein, an ARMSCOR front organization, at the Meridien Hotel in Rio de Janeiro. There they hammered out the details of the transfer. The deal was split into two segments, which were codenamed Elana I, for the shell transfer, and Elana II, for the gun acquisition. The names derived from that of "a charming hotel hostess" who served the parties their celebratory drinks at a party in the hotel's disco lounge.

The following April, ARMSCOR officials, Dennis Zeederberg of the Armaments Board among them, arrived in the North Troy offices of SRC-Vermont, where the Elana I agreement was formally signed. It was agreed that Bull would be paid $19 million for this segment of the deal, the money to be assigned to Bull's principal creditor, the First Pennsylvania Bank.

Several days later, Gerry Bull, Rodgers Gregory and General Trudeau visited the OMC office in Washington, to expedite the OMC paperwork.

By April 21, OMC Director Robinson wrote back to Bull:

> This is to confirm that your interpretation is correct that U.S. government approvals are not required with regard to contracts of your international company, acting as a marketing agent under Canadian export license to Belgium. Similarly, exports of rough, non-machined nosed forgings from the United States are not considered as falling under the purview of the U.S. munitions list...no license is required from this office for the exports of such raw materials from the United States.

The letters were so crafted that First Pennsylvania would never have to question individual shipments in the future transfers; the ruling was open-ended. As a senior bank official would later put it to American investigators, "that was critical" to their support of the Elana I project.

Next May 3, the Chamberlain Manufacturing Company, which operated the Scranton plant, asked the U.S. army Armament Command (ARMCOM) to approve production of fifty thousand forgings for SRC, "acting as an agent for Israel and other NATO countries."

Much has been made of the deal's swift approval. Surely, it is said, this must show C.I.A. involvement. The theory, while not implausible, overlooks Bull's knowledge of the approval mechanisms and the personal influence he could bring to bear. He had long-standing links with the OMC, ARMCOM, and the manufacturer. Because of his past orders for the long-nose rounds, the arsenal had production equipment already modified to produce them. Furthermore, he began negotiating the contract almost a year before the paperwork went through. He was also aided by local politics and a stagnant economy. Driven by a desire to help the financially-struggling arsenal and maintain employment for skilled personnel, ARMCOM approval came quickly. Batch One production commenced in August 1976, and continued to May 1977.

From the Scranton arsenal, truckload after truckload of the blanks headed north to the Canadian border, 450 miles away. Entering the SRC compound from the American side, the rough forgings passed into the Canadian factory, where the sophisticated lathes of Bull's high-volume machining complex smoothed and shaped them. In this process, the distinctive riding nubs that keep the shell from wobbling in the barrel were also welded on. Still gleaming from a final coat of protective varnish, the finished, empty projectiles were palletized and packed into freight containers. These rolled out the factory doors on the Canadian side, and onto waiting flatbed tractor-trailers.

From Highwater, the trucks rolled east along the St. Lawrence River, and then headed south to the Brun Term container-storage area near the docks in St. John, New Brunswick. By the end of February 1977, thirty-six full containers were waiting to continue their journey. An intercontinental web of shipping agencies, with all the characteristics of an ARMSCOR-directed operation, was about to swing into action.

At the beginning of March 1977, the freighter *SS Moura* picked up twenty of the containers from St. John, New Brunswick, and unloaded them in St. John's, Antigua, on the fourteenth of that month. A day behind it, with the remaining sixteen containers plus a meteorological van, was the motorship *Lindigger Coral*. Both shipments were stored for nearly two months in a secure dock area, guarded by the black-bereted Antigua Defence Force.

On May 24, 1977, the sleek, new, ten-thousand-ton, fast freighter, *SA Tugelaland* picked up the containers, two radar trucks, the meteorological van and assorted gun parts, in St. John's. The ship's papers said it was returning the cargo to Canada but, in reality, it sailed for South Africa, where it docked at Capetown on June 7.

The *SA Tugelaland*, which was to play a further role in the shell-transfer story, was German-registered and owned by a Hamburg firm named Globus/Reiteri. It, in turn, was controlled by SA Marine, a South African company. The *SA Tugelaland* had been leased back by Globus/Reiteri to its parent firm, which meant all the records were safely in South Africa. Even the name of the ship gave away its true origins. The obviousness of SA aside, the Tugela is a river in South Africa's Natal province.

By mid-August 1977, the shipments from Highwater had once more piled up in the St. John, New Brunswick, freight terminal. On a roundabout route that saw her dock last in New York, the *SA Tugelaland* arrived at St. John, and loaded thirty-two SRC containers.

Ten of them were empties, but the rest contained ten thousand shells. According to Canadian government records, the destination was Antigua.

One wonders if Bull or ARMSCOR paid any attention to either the irony, or the possible security risks, of using a black Caribbean nation for its transfers to the apartheid regime in South Africa. If not, it was an omission that was to cost them dearly.

On August 25, 1977, the *SA Tugelaland* docked at the Antiguan capital and deep-water port of St. John's. In the hot tropic night, the ten empty and three filled containers were unloaded. Reloading of another shipment of SRC containers, supposedly bound for Barbados, 250 miles to the south, began immediately. Beneath the glare of klieg lamps, cranes were swinging cargo containers, marked *steel forgings*, into the holds. Suddenly, there was an accident.

Now retired, dock-worker Mottley White remembers the incident well. "The crane on the dock collapsed, and the crane, the boom, everything went down into the hold...one of the containers flew open. I saw the same big bullet shells we had unloaded for this company before."

White didn't pay the incident much attention, at first. Space Research, and the nature of its cargoes, were common knowledge on the St. John's docks. But, the next day, he chanced into a disturbing conversation with some *Tugelaland* crew members. "We were on the deck," White remembers, "and the sailors, most of them is Portuguese fellow, they ask us what kind of government we have, was it black or white? We tell them, 'It is a black government.' One of them, he shake his head and point at the cargo hold. He say, 'It's a pity you have a black government that encourages shipping those things to South Africa.'"

Later that night, White received a more authoritative confirmation of the story. Leaving the ship, he wished the *Tugelaland*'s captain, Herbert Nederbrecht, a speedy return home. "Won't see it for six months," the captain said, sorrowfully. "We are going to South Africa with this cargo first."

Alarmed, White went to the port director's office, to check on the cargo's destination. "Barbados, of course," Amel Sweeny, the port director, assured him. White didn't buy it. A member of the Antiguan Workers Union, he brought the subject up at their next local meeting. There, the tale aroused both anger and interest from a union leadership politically opposed to the Antiguan government of V.C. Bird.

In October of that year, Joshua Nkomo, then a rebel leader in the fight against Ian Smith's white Rhodesian government, visited the Caribbean, and the story was told to him. A week later, he gave a news conference in Ottawa, where he charged that "nine hundred tons of arms, including mortars and machine guns," from Canada had been shipped to South Africa. While he was wrong on several points (there were only the artillery shell blanks, and there were no arms for

Rhodesia included), he was right about the *Tugelaland* and the Antiguan connection.

In September of 1979, in a televised interview with the C.B.C., Bull said flatly, "The allegations have been investigated, and refuted absolutely in a strong manner by the Governor of Antigua. The Canadian government has investigated the claim, and there's no substance to it, we've denied it every time it has arisen."

The statement indeed summarized the situation, if strictly applied to the inaccurate Nkomo claims. Further, the press discovered that the R.C.M.P. had checked out the company's shipments, and found nothing apparently wrong.

The next November, the Antiguan Workers Union gave a more accurate and detailed picture of the transfers, again naming SRC as the company involved. A flurry of stories then appeared in the North American media, in which Bull and other SRC representatives once more firmly denied any connection with South African arms shipments. They used their previous responses to the Nkomo claims, and their spurious vindication of the charges of sending weapons to Rhodesia, as a buttress for their arguments. With that, the story seemed to die. Perhaps Bull really thought things had blown over, for the shells continued to be shipped out of Highwater as regularly as before.

The arrangements were certainly changed. The scheduled visit of the *SA Tugelaland* to St. John, New Brunswick, in September or October of 1977, was canceled because of its sudden notoriety. It took some time to set the new ones up, because thirty-five thousand shells, in fifty-five containers, sat for over six months in the Brun Term depot, until March of 1988.

But, as much as Bull might have wished it, the story had not gone away; it just submerged for a few months. In Antigua, a political storm was raging over the issue, and V.C. Bird's government, now effectively run by his son, Lester Bird, was in trouble. In the beginning of 1978, the Antigua Workers Union declared a boycott of SRC test range equipment arriving aboard U.S. military-chartered vessels as part of legitimate research contracts, and Mottley White and his mates refused to unload them.

U.S. customs investigators would later determine that these refused shipments contained 1,700 155mm shell blanks, which SRC trucked from Highwater to Port Canaveral, Florida. They were added to the ship's consignment moments before the navy-leased vessel sailed.

Not only in Antigua, but throughout the Caribbean, voices were raised, demanding that SRC be banished from the island. Back in Canada, journalists, notably from the C.B.C.'s *fifth estate*, were digging further into a story their instincts told them was far from over.

While the press can be forgiven for not breaking the story before all the shipments were gone, the role of the Canadian government in allowing them to go forward is almost impossible to understand. Was Bull telling the truth in 1988, when he said, "Of course they knew what we were doing...how could we have done it otherwise?"

Within a week of Nkomo's charges in Ottawa, and coincident with the beginning of a long-term investigation by the R.C.M.P. into their affairs, SRC sought a second export permit for their shell casings at St. John, New Brunswick. Incredibly, the company was able to change the consignment destination from their own facility in Antigua to that of a sale to "the government of Spain," via a company called Barreiros Hermanos.

If there had been no suspicion of SRC's motives, it might have been comprehensible, but there was suspicion, and the R.C.M.P. smelled a rat. An ex-R.C.M.P. officer associated with the case could still get heated over the incident, more than a decade later. "There were memos sent from our Montréal office about it...warning there was a problem there...the export people either brushed them off or ignored them."

Warned though they were, the Ministries of External Affairs and Industry, Trade and Commerce approved the change of destination. No check was made to see if the sale was valid, though a phone call to the defense attaché at the Spanish embassy in Ottawa would have told them that it wasn't. One might consider that Industry, Trade and Commerce was in a similar position to the First Pennsylvania Bank. For, through CCC and the Export Development Corporation, they too had a considerable investment in SRC.

The R.C.M.P. was reduced to opening the SRC containers at the St. John docks, and checking every tenth shell to make sure they did not contain explosives. On March 7, 1978, under cover of a snowy night, some thirty-five of the shell containers were loaded on the Danish freighter *Nordferrer*, which sailed off in the direction of Europe.

So secret was the shipment that the *Nordferrer*'s captain was only advised by radio, in the sea approaches to Gibraltar, that his final destination was the Spanish Mediterranean port of Barcelona.

There, the reception of his cargo had been well prepared. An unnamed SRC official was quoted in the *Globe and Mail* of March 8, 1980, as saying it was SRC-I that ordered the shells for Barreiros Hermanos. After speculating that Lybia might have been the shells' real destination, he mentioned that Joseph Severin was instrumental in placing the Spanish order. "If he was alive," he said, "I'm sure he could tell us what happened with those orders."

But Joseph Severin had died on June 6th, 1978. Alone, he fell down some steps in Brussels late at night, while in a state of inebriation, and was found the next morning with his neck broken. While the Belgian police conducted a thorough investigation, they found no evidence of foul play. "He took a lot of secrets with him," the official told the *Globe*.

If he really had set up the Spanish end, then Severin did his last job well. In spite of all the publicity, no one figured out the transfer route, until it was far too late.

After being unloaded, the $7 million cargo was taken out of its containers, and left to sit for three months in a bonded warehouse area. No one from the Spanish government came to claim them. The *fifth estate* investigators would later find that the import documents were mysteriously missing from the files of the Barcelona customs house. They did, however, discover an export form #1869-78, showing the shells had been loaded on the motorship *SS Brizande* on June 27, with Canada given as the destination. However, the *Brizande* didn't sail for Canada. On July 27, 1978, it docked in Durban, South Africa.

Back in North America, the U.S. customs service had launched a massive investigation of SRC-Vermont, and the R.C.M.P. was close to recommending that charges be laid against SRC-Québec. Yet, SRC continued the scam to the bitter end. The remaining shells at St. John were trucked to Montréal, where they were loaded on a tiny, fifty-seven-foot, German boat, the *Atlantic River*, which sailed for Barcelona, and the same shipping agents who had handled the *Nordferrer* cargo. Within a week, the cargo was on its way to South Africa on another Danish vessel, via the Canary Islands. As far as ARMSCOR was concerned, the deal was already over.

Gerry Bull and his associates had already given South Africa the "super-gun" system it needed to defeat the Russian artillery in Angola. While there were no further attempts to overthrow the MPLA government, the Afrikaner state bought itself a decade of border "peace" for what was then its colony of Namibia (ex-German South West Africa) by turning the *Fin du Mundo* into a *cordon sanitaire*.

Every time the South West African People's Organization (SWAPO) built up logistics and training bases, to support their battle for Namibian independence, the Afrikaners raided and destroyed them. Whenever the MPLA attempted to move south and build up strength against Jonas Savimbi's UNITA, its forces were decimated. Sometimes the South Africans would fight with UNITA, other times alone. There are even reports that they occasionally destroyed fighting units of their erstwhile ally. Perhaps it was to underscore some subtle message, maybe to keep them from getting too strong.

For South Africa sought no victory, only chaos, and its purpose was to keep southern Angola bleeding. The name of the game was destabilization and scorched earth. No one will ever know how many thousands of innocent civilians perished in the conflict. Schools, hospitals, farms and churches became targets for South African firepower, often at higher priority levels than strictly military targets.

More than one road in southern Angola would see severed hands nailed to the trees beside it, with signs in Afrikaans declaring, *VER-DAMKE KAFFIR*—to hell with niggers. Many of the people of southern Angola and Namibia are animists, a quasi-religious spiritual outlook that believes if one's body is not buried whole, the soul cannot go on.

The G-5 made it all possible. For, whether SADF came in heliborne commando raids or armored columns racing up the roads, all of it was covered by batteries of G-5 guns and its self-propelled variant, the G-6 Rhino.

The Rhino, or the Kalahari Ferrari, as its crews nicknamed it, was a nine-meter-long vehicle that ran on six huge, twenty-one by twenty-five tires. Capable of traveling the great distances of the *Fin du Mundo* at speeds up to ninety kilometers per hour, it provided a strategic cover force, capable of rapid response and great concentration.

Whether towed or self-propelled, the long barrels and their aeroballistic shells were SADF's magic umbrella, its shield and protection. Supported by a scratch force of Forward Air Controllers, flying civilian light aircraft, to identify over-the-horizon targets, they destroyed rocket launcher and artillery positions with a rain of fire that the Cuban and Angolan gunners were helpless to respond to.

In Angola, Stalin's God of War and Gerry Bull's creations spoke louder than any Canadian diplomatic initiative or pious speech at the United Nations. As one cynic put it, the G-5 was "Canada's greatest contribution to solving the problems of southern Africa." Is it any wonder that Bull's name is better known in Angola than in the nation of his birth?

CHAPTER 13

By April 4, 1979, when South Africa publicly announced it had commenced production of the G-5 gun, most of the details of the shell transfers had been reported in the media, and the results of investigations, by at least six Canadian and American agencies or investigative bodies, were being leaked on a regular basis. Yet, it would take years before the European side of the operation, and its vital importance to South Africa, would become clear. As late as 1982, the staff report of the U.S. congressional committee would state that their investigators "came to believe" that PRB "in fact provided the double-based propellant charges for the SRC-produced shells...and that they were filled in South Africa."

This was true, as far as it went, but the investigators missed the transfer of manufacturing technology, and profoundly misunderstood the mechanics of the financial arrangements, which resulted in ARMSCOR owning twenty percent of Canadian Technical Industries (CTI).

The European part of the conspiracy was so shrouded in secrecy, so hidden behind false fronts and the confusion of international boundaries and corporate warfare, that much of the tale would remain buried for over a decade. It would only emerge in 1990, when the Green Party of Austria obtained documentary evidence from the arms export trial of the country's biggest industrial conglomerate, Voest-Alpine.

Elana-II, the gun component of the deal struck in Rio, also included the propellant part of the transfer. South Africa's Sommerset Chemicals (SOMCHEM) is known to have been producing these charges as early as 1978, a process that English defense writer John Reed describes as "a remarkably rapid acquisition of capability." For, while South Africa, a mining nation, had a long-established ability to produce civilian explosives, the production of modern, doubled-based military propellants requires special machinery and expertise. One of the many technical differences is that the material must be formed like small strands of hollow spaghetti, to increase the surface area available for burning.

Europe provided a multiple-source base for the machinery required, some of which is remarkably similar to the mixing equipment used in large bakeries. PRB had both the production expertise and the knowledge of where to buy the equipment.

Further expertise was provided by Valleyfield Chemical Products. In the company of technicians from SRC-Q, its president, Jean Vezina, and other staff members are known to have visited South Africa at least twice in 1978. In 1979, Vezina admitted that the trips had taken place, but he resolutely refused to comment on their nature.

The financial aspects of Elana I and II are better understood by looking at who participated in the meeting at the Hotel Meridien in Rio, in March 1976. Besides Gerry Bull, Joseph Severin, president of PRB, attended, as did Paul Rigo, head of PRB's defense-products division and their representative on the Board of Directors of SRC-International. Louis Palacio, who helped Bull design long-range sub-caliber rounds for 155mm guns, at SRC-Québec, and had been associated with the HARP project at McGill, was present in his new role as president of SRC-I.

In collusion with the South African representatives, appearing in their guise as Colet Trading of Liechtenstein, these participants agreed to reorganize SRC-I, so that it would be able to handle various aspects of the transfers, including payments. It was also provisionally agreed that South Africa would purchase a twenty-percent interest in CTI of Montréal, to satisfy Bull's creditors, and keep SRC-Q's operations alive.

The Bull family has always denied the South African financial involvement in CTI, in the strongest terms. In 1987, Michael Bull told Dyllon Roach that it was a lie, and threatened legal action to anyone saying it. "Be careful what you print," he warned.

That same year, however, his father gave this weak-voiced and hesitant answer to the question. "I wouldn't know...you'd have to talk to the lawyers in Philadelphia about that...I just worked on my science."

The cash-transfer mechanism followed the usual diffuse and complex arrangements that had, by now, become characteristic of Bull's operations. According to the *Globe and Mail* of March 11, 1980, Jack Frost helped set up a Dutch-registered company "in the early 1970s," called Space Capital Investments SA (SCI). According to Frost, SCI was "a dummy company...set up as a money mover." Quoting an unnamed SRC-Q official, the *Globe* said SCI's managing director was Jacques Heymans, and that the company had been set up to "sell anti-riot and crowd-control equipment to the South African government." Why a company selling such gear would call itself Space Capital Investments was not explained; nor why that name would be picked "in the early 1970s."

Whenever it was set up, and whatever reasons the participants might have given for its founding, SCI was definitely available for use as an ARMSCOR front organization. According to a copyrighted story in the February 14, 1980, edition of *The Burlington Free Press*, there was a large and extraordinary meeting in the London branch offices of the First Pennsylvania Bank, on July 6 and 7, 1977. Besides Gerry Bull and Jean Vezina, who was appearing as SRC-Q's chief financial officer, Montréal lawyer Lambert Toupin, counsel for the Bull family, was there. Also present were three members of the Philadelphia law firm of Montgomery, McCracken, who represented Bull's interests in Pennsylvania. Among those representing First Pennsylvania were vice president Albert Lusen and David Harwi from Saul and Ewing, the bank's lawyers. Donald Martin, head of Burlington's WEZF TV station, a minor investor from the earliest days of SRC, also attended.

Representing SCI were Frank Nel, J.S. Coetzee, manager of commercial sales for ARMSCOR, and Montréal lawyer Marcel Paquette, a long-time friend of Bull's. Frank Nel, almost certainly a South African, was a less definable figure. He would shortly be appointed a vice-president of Shefford Electronics, and become ARMSCOR's watchdog on the Canadian end of the project. The *Free Press* quoted an SRC-Q source as saying, "I was told he was a Belgian...He was given the real VIP treatment. He even occupied Bull's office [in Montréal] for a time." Nel left the firm under "mysterious circumstances," in November of 1979 and, according to the *Free Press*, Canadian immigration officials could find no record of Nel ever having entered Canada.

The purpose of the meeting was to dispose of the $10 million investment SCI was making in CTI. As a result of these complicated, and often contentious, negotiations, the South Africans were given 545,970 shares of preferred stock in CTI for some $3 million, while the remainder was secured by a $7 million debenture from CTI.

For its part, First Pennsylvania received a total of $6.3 million in cash, and was relieved of a $3.7 million letter-of-credit obligation to SRC. In return, First Pennsylvania returned to CTI all mortgages, company stock and patents it was holding as collateral. It also released a number of insurance policies that it was holding on Bull's life. Then it handed over an $8.6 million letter of credit from the South African Volkskas Bank of Pretoria, which it was holding until the SCI funds were paid. According to Lunsen "there were so many things to sign...John Seigrist [of the bank] signed for me [at times]. It was just a matter of who was tired of signing. When we finished, the wires were sent and the money was transferred."

This meeting solved the problems of financing Elana I, the shell transfer that SRC ran under the internal code-name of "Miami." But what of Elana II, the gun and propellant technology transfer? The *Free Press* article mentions a previous $13 million payment from the Volkskas Bank in "a related transfer," which occurred in 1975, the very year the South African drive on Luanda collapsed. Other sources had stated that this payment went to PRB, to pay for the initial propellant contract and their aid in transferring manufacturing technology to SOMCHEM.

But that was long-finished business by 1979. While the law-enforcement agencies of Canada and the U.S. slowly closed the ring around SRC, Bull was spending more and more of his time in Europe. Increasingly, the destination was Vienna. Through the good offices of Shoul Eisenberg, aided by Philippe Bull and Dr. Erben, Bull was talking to Voest-Alpine about their desire to form a new division to produce military equipment.

Employing some seventy thousand people, state-owned Voest-Alpine is one of Europe's largest steel producers. It is also a "turn key" builder of industrial plants, in fields as diverse as petrochemicals, medicine and electronics. To Bull, it must have seemed that he had finally found a major player, who would turn his designs into an open, legitimate reality. If so, he was to be sadly disappointed.

The Vienna court documents tell a tale of corporate struggle and double-dealing, on the part of PRB and Voest-Alpine, versus Bull and SRC-Q. For much of this conflict, SRC-I was the major battlefield. Tied in with other information, the documents also reveal the cynical *realpolitik* of the Austrian and Canadian governments, when it came to jobs and money.

In an interview in the October 1986 issue of *MILITARY TECHNOLOGY* magazine, a senior Voest-Alpine executive stated, "In May 1979, we decided to commence manufacture of artillery pieces...we then acquired a license for a particular weapon, and started up straightaway with an order for thirteen guns from Thailand."

By April 9, 1979, Voest-Alpine was writing to Gerry Bull, as an officer of SRC-I, "...we hereby confirm our preparedness in principle to:

1. Purchase 1/3 interest in SRC-I as per the option stated on your memorandum of 29 March.
2. Purchase 20 % of Canadian Technical Industries (CTI) for the same price as paid by Space Capital Investments (SCI) in July 1977, that is, a total investment of 10,000,000—US $.
3. Purchase the SCI interests in CTI for 10,000,000—US $."

The following May 19, Voest-Alpine (hereafter referred to as V-A) sent CTI a draft agreement, whose first purpose was "to assure the Canadian government that V-A is a partner of CTI." Secondly, it repeated the offer to buy twenty percent of CTI. It also stated the need to "clarify the relationships between the "Thai Government, CCC (Canadian Commercial Corp.), SRC-Q and Voest-Alpine." In addition it made the following points:

— V-A guarantees performance of Thai gun contract to CCC.
— V-A and SRC-Q personnel [will] cooperate in Canada on the first two guns.
— V-A will be paid for this work by the Canadian Government.

While CCC had signed an agreement with SRC-Q on March 15 of that year, to initiate production of the GC-45 order for Thailand, it quickly came to the conclusion that SRC-Q was not capable of finishing the job. The increasing publicity about the ARMSCOR scandal, and the firm's shaky finances, had combined with the realization that SRC-Q had only produced a prototype weapon, not one that could be manufactured in a cost-effective way. To fulfil its role as guarantor to the Thais, CCC, since it could not find another Canadian company capable of producing the order, was forced to turn to SRC-Q's prospective partner, V-A, as a manufacturer.

However, unknown to CCC, there were other, far larger, orders for the GC-45 on the horizon. By the fall, PRB and V-A finished a series of meetings that resulted in a September 5 Memorandum of Understanding between the two firms. In it, PRB agreed to provide V-A with a "clear and complete description of the maze of connections, rights and commitments existing between SRC-Q—PRB—SRC-I," and "a brief 'status report' on the Saudi negotiations." It asked, "Is V-A willing to manufacture these guns? At what price? According to which delivery schedule?" PRB also wanted to know just what V-A was doing, talking to CTI and SRC-Q about the Thai contract. The answer was that V-A was "simply committed to make ten guns, which will be exact copies of the two units now being manufactured in the U.S.A." In spite of the legalese and the polite formulations, the mutual suspicion of both parties in the talks is obvious.

They were not the only people who were getting suspicious. On September 17, Gerry Bull wrote to V-A executives Lettner and Cranz, as an officer of SRC-Q. The subject was "Discussions in Canada, with SRC-Q and the Canadian Government." It's tone was almost pleading:

> Without appearing unduly critical, let me comment that it seems somewhat confusing that V-A sends different personnel to each meeting [who] lack the background of our previous discussions...and start off on paths which lead us to conclusions regarding
>
> i) V-A's real intent
> ii) V-A's confidence in us that are not positive.
>
> I feel that is absolutely necessary to ensure that no basis be built for misunderstanding...It would appear to me that a 'primary' decision must be made...It is the 'go' or 'no go' decision...I thought we had long passed that stage, and must admit surprise and shock to find we are back there...
>
> Immediate sorting out of SRC-I and SRC-Q relations to V-A are imperative...SRC-I designated PRB to prime this [the Saudi] contract. PRB have stalled, owing to internal problems. Bluntly, I am now led to believe that PRB cannot sign any significant contract until...their internal management problems are resolved. Thus both the Saudi Arabia and Somali contracts are in jeopardy. Specifically
>
> 1) Saudi Arabia:
>   [78 guns]
>   30,000 to 50,000 rounds of ammunition
>   Value [gross] $150,000,000 U.S.
> 2) Somali:
>   [64 guns]
>   Ammunition not yet specified
>   Value [gross] $100,000,000

Bull went on to say that he thought V-A should "take over SRC-I with SRC-Q by picking up at least the 1/3 shares." Later, in reference to the proposed V-A investment in SRC-Q, via CTI, he wrote, "The Canadian government has shown its willingness to aid V-A participation. Thus the political climate is good; the domestic market is assured to SRC-Q and could be about 50% of its total gross."

If nothing else, the last statements show that Bull was trying to whistle his way past the graveyard. The political climate was anything but good, and CCC realized it had a hot potato on its hands that it had to get rid of. There were political and international implications which, if exposed, could portray Canada's loudly-voiced opposition to apartheid as mere window dressing to please simple clerics and human-rights advocates.

As they argued with one another, neither Bull nor PRB understood that they were midgets, dealing with a giant that wasn't interested in buying into them; all it wanted was their technology. Especially in the case of SRC-Q, V-A was more than willing to participate in crushing them, if it lowered the end cost.

The nebulous and never-to-materialize quarter-billion dollars worth of gun and shell orders that Bull referred to were provided by a long-time associate of Shoul Eisenberg, Saad Gabir. Later referred to in the media as "a mysterious Arab," his actual origins are unknown. He got his start in the arms business by selling surplus Nazi war equipment, left over from Rommel's campaigns in the deserts of North Africa. A multi-millionaire with a wide range of business investments, Gabir became a landed immigrant in Canada in 1978. After making several highly profitable investments in real estate and manufacturing, Gabir soon developed powerful friends among both Conservative and Liberal Members of Parliament. A member of the international fundamentalist Muslim Brotherhood, Gabir had extensive business interests in Pakistan, and was a confidant of General Zia ul Haq, then Pakistan's military ruler. Strangely, later events would show this man to be kinder to Gerry Bull than many of his long-time associates.

On October 5, 1979, there was a meeting, in Brussels, of the board of directors of SRC-I. Paul Rigo of PRB had the chair, while a "Mr. Rousseff" (probably Gabir) was present as an observer. Louis Palacio presented details of a licensing agreement, provisionally signed between V-A and SRC-Q on May 30. In return for the promised $10 million investment in CTI, Bull had agreed to turn over the GC-45 rights to V-A, without any further royalties! The minutes state that, "after some discussion," the board accepted this, in return for a writing-down of the paper debt SRC-I owed to SRC-Q.

Worse was to follow. The provisional V-A SRC-Q deal referred to an initial downpayment of $2 million. When the final agreement was signed between SRC-I, V-A and SRC-Q on November 19, there was a clause inserted, stating that, if any of the parties involved went bankrupt, all rights would devolve without further compensation to the remaining partners. Since neither V-A or PRB (whose rights the deal acknowledged) were in any danger of going bottom-up, that left SRC-Q as the obvious candidate.

Gerry Bull should have seen it coming, but events would show that he walked into the trap with astonishing naïveté. Perhaps he could not conceive that the Canadian government would treat him the way it did.

On September 21, 1979, Voest-Alpine and SRC-Q were the subject of another meeting. At 10:00 A.M., on the seventeenth floor of Ottawa's Place de Ville tower, item 2.3 on the CCC's board of directors agenda was "SRC Thailand Contract: Status Report."

In 1990, David Todd, a journalist with Southam News Services, found a heavily deleted copy of the official minutes of this meeting in an old file, obtained by Southam under Canada's Access to Information Act, in pursuit of an unrelated story.

In a January 4, 1991, telephone conversation with this author, Christian Sarrazin, CCC's Vice President for Corporate Affairs, and Jean-Pierre Cloutier, their General Counsel and Secretary, filled in the blanks. The underlined sections are either what they agree is in the official minutes, or what they say is the correct wording. The text presented here is in the same letter spacing as the document obtained by Southam.

> The President presented Agenda Item 2.3
> "SRC Thailand Contract : Status Report".
>
> With respect to a $2 million-dollar
> infusion of funds by Voest-Alpine from
> Austria to SEC, as a deposit against
> its intention to purchase 20 per cent
> of SRC-Q   , Mrs. Bata cautioned the
> meeting that such a partnership would
> give Voest-Alpine   access to badly
> needed technology to be exported from
> Austria in due course, in competition
> with Canada. She, therefore, considered
> the amount of $2 million insufficient.
> Furthermore, if the arrangement were to
> include the supply of ammunition, it could
> create a potentially dangerous situation
> which would not be in the best interest
> of either Canada or Austria.
>
> The members were informed that the agree-
> ment was for Asia only and that Voest-
> Alpine's market share was contractually
> restricted to specific markets which had
> little interest for Canada. Mr. Allan
> indicated that all munitions for V-A's
> guns would have to be purchased in Canada.

Even allowing for some possible inaccuracies in CCC's collective memory, the minutes reveal that Mrs. Sonya Bata (of shoe-company fame) was prescient enough to see that Canada was giving away something more than a gun contract. Mr. Sarrazin said, "From what I read here, her point seems to have been that possibly we are creating a competitor abroad...[asking] aren't we giving a non-Canadian company the capability to compete with potential Canadian suppliers? Allen tried to answer that in saying the market for which V-A has the technology, and the rights to sell, are limited."

Voest-Alpine would have been surprised to hear that, since they were negotiating on sales of GC-45 guns in Africa and the Middle East. It is true that Annex 3 of the licensing agreement signed November 19, 1979, between V-A, PRB, SRC-I and SRC-Q, did not give V-A any rights in Canada, the U.S., the Caribbean, or most of South America, nor in Asian countries like Thailand and Taiwan. However, this agreement was to be negated by SRC's bankruptcy, the next year.

Mr. Sarrazin, who was not with CCC at the time, strenuously denies that they had any knowledge of South African involvement in SRC. To believe that, one has to assume that none of its board members watched television or read newspapers. What was Mrs. Bata's "...potentially dangerous situation which would not be in the best interest of either Canada or Austria."?

In fairness to CCC, it must be pointed out that they did have a legal obligation to complete a legitimate export agreement for Thailand, and Voest-Alpine did successfully complete that order. On the other hand, V-A ended up with unencumbered rights to the GC-45 and its ammunition, for the paltry sum of $2 million, when CCC helped put the CTI group of companies into bankruptcy the next year.

No wonder V-A's sales manager would tell *MILITARY TECHNOLOGY*, in 1986, that the Thai order "was naturally a pleasant introductory accompaniment to our entry into the [artillery] business."

All through the negotiations, it is clear that Voest-Alpine had a better appreciation of the growing ARMSCOR scandal, and its likely effect on SRC-Q, than Bull did. They were certainly aware of their own government's reservations about being involved with SRC. Considering that the company's decisions were vetted by the Austrian government, and that Dr. Thomas Nowotny, the Austrian consul general in New York, had personally informed Chancellor Kreisky about the growing storm around SRC, their actions show a cold, Machiavellian logic.

Profil would describe them as "out-maneuvering" the Austrian government. V-A stressed that the new gun-production facilities would be located in Linz, a region of high unemployment and political problems for Kreisky's party. Nevertheless, the chancellor still had reservations. In January of 1980, he wrote to another government offical that there could be "bad aftershocks" from the association, and that he might be "personally blamed."

It would take eight years, and a major war in the Middle East, before his prophecy would be fulfilled. It was only then that the consequences of allowing Voest-Alpine to become an export-oriented military manufacturer would hammer home.

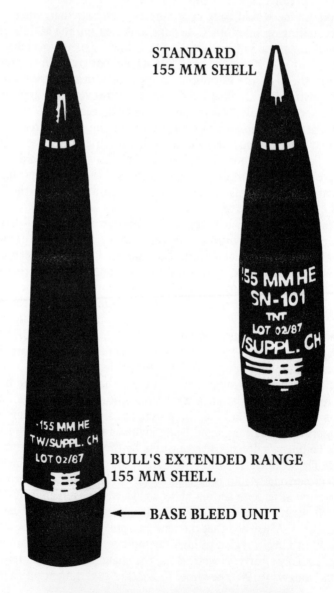

STANDARD
155 MM SHELL

BULL'S EXTENDED RANGE
155 MM SHELL

← BASE BLEED UNIT

CHAPTER 14

C.I.A. does not have, and never has had, any connection to SRC.

—Frank Calucci, Deputy C.I.A. Director, to the U.S. State Department, in 1979

In the spring of 1978, Michael Bull graduated with honors from Laval University with a Bachelor's degree in Business Administration, at the age of twenty-two. During that summer and fall, he completed his examinations for a degree in chartered accountancy, and then went to work for a Québec City auditing firm. Michael did not see much of his father during this period of his life. The son describes their relationship at the time as "somewhat distant...maybe cool might be the word."

Gerry Bull's patriarchal instincts, the belief that it was a parent's duty to guide his children's destinies, had collided with his son's desire to find his own course in life. His father had not approved of him switching from biology to business administration, nor did he like his choice of schools. As Michael put it, "I was proceeding with my own independent career. I have a strong character, and my father also, so we clashed on a number of occasions."

Yet Michael, in light of his future role in his father's business, gained a unique insight into Gerry Bull's outlooks, at the time. The picture is one of a man whose focus and perceptions had narrowed to the point where he could not see the path that his restless energy was hurling him down. Bull had become so immersed in the tactical expedients of keeping his operations alive, and trying to drum up future business, that he stubbornly refused to consider the storm outside as anything other than a annoyance to be brushed aside. Elana II and Miami were over, what did it matter now?

Asked how his father could have been so blind as not to see where the course of events was taking him, Michael answered, "Hindsight is perfect sight...Things that look obvious to the objective eye today, did not look obvious to the objective eye then. Keeping in mind that my father was under tremendous pressure...the government, the civil servants, are very, very good at...[smoothing things over]...I grant them a little bit of credit, as well, for sincerity...some of them truly believed in my father; unfortunately, they were quite a minority. But it's these people who kept my father going. They didn't necessarily do it maliciously. Of course, there were a lot of them who didn't like my father, and deliberately misguided him. Unfortunately, they outnumbered the first ones...It's so obvious now, but it's the combination of struggling to survive...when you're drowning in the pond, you'll look at every twig to be your savior. If your worst enemy says, 'Look behind you, there's one,' you'll grab it."

R.C.M.P. Staff Sergeant Ed Noel, who retired from the Mounties in 1981, headed the Canadian investigation into Space Research. He told CTV's *W5*, in late 1980, that it took him two years to trace the complicated paper trail that Bull and his associates had left, and even then, the investigation was less than satisfactory.

"Well, the first two shipments we were investigating, the two shipments on the *Tugelaland*, which left St. John's, New Brunswick, in May and August 1976, traveled to Antigua, and eventually ended up in South Africa. There could have been part of the shipment that remained in Antigua. They were off-loaded, and there was other equipment on-loaded. We can't definitely establish what left Antigua."

Without denigrating Staff Sergeant Noel's personal effort to establish the facts, the statement speaks volumes about the inadequacy of the resources available to the R.C.M.P., for investigating an affair that involved a half-dozen countries, and had political and economic implications for the Canadian government.

External Affairs and the Ministry of Industry, Trade and Commerce, warned though they had been by the R.C.M.P. about the dubiousness of at least some of Bull's shell exports via St. John's, were initially unwilling to interfere with the operations of a firm that they had a legitimate financial stake in. Considering Bull's close association with the Department of National Defence, the soldiers tended to believe the tale that the owner of their only indigenous propellant and explosives plant was involved in a secret operation for Canada's closest ally, and that a blind eye was the appropriate response. For the politicians, a messy trial, and international outrage over what would appear to be Canadian hypocrisy, was not a pleasant prospect. Gerry Bull was not alone in hoping it would all blow over.

It was the press that kept the story alive, and would finally force the government to act. While increasingly frustrated R.C.M.P. officers helped the process, by a series of judicious leaks, it was journalists who established, at least in the public eye, what left Antigua, and where it went.

While much of their work was later to be buried, the Mounties sensed, from the beginning of their queries, that SRC was "dirty." When first attempting to trace the shell shipments, they asked the company to turn over the gun barrels used for test firings in Antigua. Since SRC well knew that wear and calibration measurements on the barrels could establish approximately how many shells were actually consumed in the supposed tests, they told the R.C.M.P. that the worn-out tubes had been dumped in the ocean after the firing series. "That's when we began to smell a rat," one R.C.M.P. source told *The Burlington Free Press.*

The R.C.M.P. agents, who visited Antigua in 1977 and 1978, received little assistance from a government that was frantically trying to distance itself from SRC, as well as cover up its role in facilitating the shell transfers. Friendly monologues about Caribbean cultural attitudes toward record-keeping, and contradictory statements from St. John port director Amal Sweeney, were all they got. On September 12, 1978, Lester Bird, acting as premier, in place of his ailing father, would write to the Canadian High Commissioner in Barbados, stating that, "unfortunately, the Royal Canadian Mounted Police received incomplete and inaccurate documents from us, as at the time we were ourselves trying to pull the threads of the situation together."

Belgium and Spain were only marginally better. While these nations showed the visiting Canadians their work on the investigation of Barreros Hermanos, which related to a possible shipment of Belgian FN rifles to South Africa the previous year, they were loath to be involved in an affair that could reflect badly on their national reputations. The Belgians especially, because of their traditional *laissez faire* attitudes on arms sales, viewed the investigations as mere technical violations of foreign regulations that "had no relevance to the legal operations of legal entities in Belgium." Since no charges were being considered in Brussels, the authorities shrugged and murmured their regrets.

At home, the investigation was hampered by the reluctance of SRC employees to say anything that could harm a man some of them came close to worshiping. Others, with business ties to SRC, were also uncooperative. Inspector Donald Docker, head of the R.C.M.P.'s Customs and Excise Investigations Section in Ottawa, told *The Globe and Mail*, in March of 1980, that "the investigation has been hampered by the reluctance of some professionals, such as lawyers and accountants, to give information unless they are compelled to do so by a court."

The American probe of Bull's activities began soon after Nkomo's accusations in Ottawa. Because of their greater resources, they not only accomplished more, their investigations helped keep the Canadian one alive. By the end of 1977, the State Department, the C.I.A. and the U.S. army had launched their own internal investigations of SRC. However, it was the U.S. Treasury Department, in cooperation with the F.B.I. and the American Department of Justice, that took the lead in determining whether charges should be laid against Bull and SRC-Vermont.

In mid-1978, American customs investigators descended on Antigua and Barbados. With the cooperation of the State Department, and the use of their embassy resources in the Caribbean, it did not take them long to establish the facts of the case. Especially important to them was the extensive assistance SRC had received, either wittingly or unwittingly, from the U.S. army. The use of army-chartered transport vessels to move equipment and shells into Antigua figured largely in their queries.

On July 12, 1979, John Eddy, the deputy chief of the U.S. mission in Barbados, paid a visit to Antigua and laid the story before Premier Vere Bird. The aged man appeared genuinely staggered. According to an article in the August 12, 1979, *Toronto Star*, Bird stared silently out a window for several minutes, before whispering, "This is difficult. I will be in serious trouble."

That afternoon, as Eddy was waiting at the local airport for a flight back to Barbados, he was accosted by a chunky, powerfully-built black man, who told Eddy he knew of his meeting with Bird, and that Eddy should "back off." To add emphasis to the point, he opened his jacket to reveal a .38 pistol tucked into his pants.

The man was another of those strays that Gerry Bull had developed a penchant for picking up. An American citizen, Warren Hart had publicly claimed, the year before, to have been a spy for the F.B.I. and the R.C.M.P. in the late sixties and early seventies. His work involved infiltrating left-wing black-power groups in the U.S. and Canada. Most noticeable was his appearance at Montréal's Sir George Williams University, where he posed as a bodyguard for Roosevelt Douglas, a

Grenadian student who was arrested over the destruction of the university computer center, in 1967. What had brought him his brief flurry of notoriety in Canada was his secret taping of an innocuous meeting, in 1978, between several black student leaders and John Rodriguez, the NDP Member of Parliament for Nickel Belt.

According to a March 10, 1980, *Globe and Mail* article, Hart was hired by SRC in March, 1978. Not only did he work closely with the Antiguan police, he tried to win popular support for the company by spending money on community projects like volleyball courts and uniforms for local soccer teams. Quickly recognized, and denounced as a spy by local left-wing activists, he nevertheless continued his activities on behalf of SRC; work that went beyond organizing soccer matches.

Cosmos Phillips, the Antiguan attorney-general, finally asked Hart to leave the island, after a high-powered .22 rifle with a telescopic sight was discovered in a shipment of soccer jerseys. It was claimed that Hart intended to use the weapon to assassinate Tim Hector, a leader of the Antiguan Caribbean Liberation Movement (ACLM) and the person who had first denounced him as a police informer.

Hart was not the only person who threatened American investigators on behalf of SRC. In August of 1978, Carlton Braithwaite visited John Eddy, at the American embassy in Barbados. He told him about the "tragic accident" that had happened to "an SRC employee in Brussels," who had died after falling down a flight of stairs. Eddy asked Braithwaite if the man had had a drinking problem. "No," Braithwaite replied, "people die in funny ways." While Joseph Severin was not an SRC employee, Braithwaite had precisely summed up the circumstances of his demise, the previous July.

As much as SRC tried to fight it, it is obvious that Bull never understood the dynamics of the political storm that was raging in the Caribbean over his schemes. To *The Burlington Free Press* of October 21, 1979, he said "it was communists in Antigua," who were behind the allegations against him. While the political spectrum could be stretched to make that true, in a broad sense, the outlook concentrated on the delivery-man and ignored the message. Selling arms to South Africa was something that no decent Antiguans, whatever their political stripe, could support. Within a year, SRC's operations in both Antigua and Barbados would be history.

Back home, the U.S. army refused to cooperate with the customs investigators. A source told the *Free Press* that, "It was like running into a brick wall...I gave it up. It's their problem and they ought to check it out, but they won't."

A spokesman for the Defense Department told the press that "the army's activities in regard to Space Research were in accordance with both army policy and the law."

Others, knowledgable in military procurement procedures, disagreed. "There's no question they violated their regulations," one procurement expert said.

No matter how glacially the investigations proceeded, there was a massive inevitability about them. Questions about SRC were being asked as far afield as the Security Council of the United Nations and the White House. In the fall of 1978, President Jimmy Carter told a press conference, "If it [the allegations about SRC] should prove true, and if the Pentagon has any role to play in it, directly or indirectly, I would use my full influence to comply with the UN resolution."

On December 7, 1978, U.S. prosecutors felt confident enough to present their case to a federal grand jury, convened in Rutland, Vermont. So voluminous was the documentation, and so long was the parade of witnesses, that it took until March 25, 1980, for the U.S. government to finally lay charges against Bull, Rodgers Gregory and SRC (U.S.) in the U.S. District Court at Rutland.

Robert Bennet, a prominent Washington attorney, and local lawyer Anthony Lamb, had been hired to defend Bull, Gregory and SRC (U.S.). Considering the years of work behind the investigations, the five allegations the government made were remarkably brief. Flanked by their lawyers, Bull and Gregory listened impassively, as U.S. Attorney William B. Grey read the charges before Judge James Holden:

> Between April 7, 1976, and September 10, 1978, in the District of Vermont, SPACE RESEARCH CORPORATION (U.S.), now known as Saber Industries Inc., GERALD V. BULL and RODGERS L. GREGORY, the defendants, willfully did export and cause to be exported from the United States of America to the Republic of South Africa, without being licensed for such export by the Department of State...articles designated by the United States Munitions List [Title 22, Code of Federal Regulations, Part 121.01], that is, arms, ammunition and implements of war, and components and technology therefor, namely:
>
> At least thirty thousand (30,000) 155 millimeter extended range projectile forgings and components thereof
>
> Two (2) 155 milimeter gun barrels
>
> One (1) radar tracking system consisting of two (2) vans.

The following four charges dealt with the details of how SRC and it's officers "knowingly and wilfully did make a writing...containing false information in a matter within the jurisdiction of the United States Customs Service."

After the charges were read, the defendants' lawyers, who had conducted extensive prior negotiations with the justice department, nodded to their clients, and the two men rose to face the court.

At this juncture, it must be pointed out that there is a misconception about Bull's court appearances that the media, and even Mimi Bull, inadvertently propagate to this day. They constantly refer to "Bull's trial." Gerry Bull never had a trial. On the advice of their lawyers, he and Gregory pleaded guilty to the charges on the first day of the proceedings, which meant that the government never had to present its evidence against them.

After accepting the defendants' guilty pleas, Judge Holden approved the holding of sentence negotiations between the prosecutors and Bull's lawyers. He then ordered the defendants bound over for sentencing on June 16. Bull and Gregory were released on a personal recognizance of $35,000 each. The only restriction placed on them was that "the defendant shall contact his attorney and notify him of his whereabouts every ten days."

When Bull and Gregory returned to Judge Holden's court two months later, SRC (U.S.) was fined $45,000, and Bull and Gregory, as its chief officers, were sentenced to a year's incarceration. The judge insisted that "six months must be served in a jail-type institution." The record of the court proceedings says, "Mr. Bull states he has read the pre-sentence report and waives statements...Mr. Bull states there is no reason why sentence should not be imposed." Judge Holden then ordered that "the defendant Bull is to voluntarily surrender to the custody of the Attorney General at the institution designated by the Attorney General by noon on July 30, 1980."

Sam Hemmingway, of *The Burlington Free Press*, was at the Rutland courthouse that day. A decade later, he still vividly remembers Bull's reaction to the jail term. "He was composed in the courtroom...there was no gesturing or signs of emotion...but he was definitely upset with what was happening to him...he was stunned."

There is a television newstape of Bull, emerging from the courthouse to face a score of journalists and a half-dozen anti-apartheid demonstrators. Head hunched forward, he raced down the steps, shaking off the restraining hand of one of his lawyers, who was obviously surprised at Bull's sudden, violent moves. Turning left, almost running alongside a high mesh fence, his whole attitude was one of rage. His face, when he turned back toward the camera, was contorted into a black fury directed at anyone who came close to him.

As Hemmingway recalls, "When he was asked for a comment about what had gone on; that's when he was obviously angry at the media, and told us basically to get lost. He physically pushed a mike out of his face, and raised a fist toward me. He stopped and took a step toward me...I think he was about to hit me...then his lawyer ran up and persuaded him to get into the car instead."

The incident was symptomatic of a larger problem. Racked by rage, despair and frustration, Gerry Bull had entered the darkest period of his life, weeks before he cursed the press from the steps of the Rutland courthouse.

The trouble began coincident with his first court appearance, in March. As he rose, when Judge Holden left the court, the terrible reality of where the legal process was taking him must have finally sunk in. All the advice from his powerful friends that "it would be worked out," and that he "should not worry about it," was revealed as the type of lies casual acquaintances tell those with terminal diseases. Saying "guilty," when he did not believe, or could not admit, that he was, had a traumatic effect on this once-supremely confident man. Bull, who knew in his heart it was a mistake, nevertheless followed the advice of his Washington attorney, an action he was to regret to his dying day. For that single word, when spoken in a court of law, has a finality that can seldom be taken back.

Gerry Bull was nearly crushed by the events leading up to his imprisonment. The impact can be compared to the effect of his mother's death on the father he had both loved and hated. Like his father, he would recover; like his father, he would never be the same again.

Abetted by leaked comments from the government's attorneys, most of the media would form the cynical impression that Bull's rage and the resultant nervous breakdown, which led to his admission to a Connecticut mental institution, were "a courtroom maneuver," designed to avoid punishment. But Bull's mental collapse was no fake. The travail he went through has been testified to by too many people for it to have been a put-on. He had long been a drinker; a man who liked to party and get drunk. Now, what he had previously done for pleasure, suddenly became a search for refuge. Michael Bull would say that his dad had become "terribly depressed in those years...he did drink heavily for a while."

Mimi Bull described it in gentler terms. "Gerry had been under a lot of pressure before the trial because, financially, everything was blocked, and he wanted to save the company, save the jobs, keep it going until things got cleared up, and he did not pay much attention to allegations made at him and his right-hand man [Rodgers Gregory] there..."

Mimi still feels strongly that Gerry was badly advised by Bennet. "He was called back from Europe to plead guilty, and he didn't even have a minute to think about it. He had twenty-four hours before he was in court pleading guilty. He was told it was the best thing, although I was against it...I was away and managed to get back here too late to tell him not to plead guilty."

As to his condition at the time, she said, "He was completely exhausted and he needed rest...I think he wanted to take back his plea, so he was working very hard on that while he was in the clinic. It was not a nervous breakdown; it was just physical rundown. When you get in those clinics, the first thing they do is put you in isolation, and they treat you as if you are under a very bad breakdown, but they didn't realize that that was not the case."

In the months before his trial, Bull was in a number of protracted meetings with Canadian government officials over the fate of his companies, which added to his worries. According to Mimi, "He was feeling terrible because of all the stress; he couldn't sleep without sleeping pills and he was under pressure. The grand jury had gone on for a year and a half, and all the funds were cut, and he had to do everything to sell technology to try to save the company.

"Through all this [there were] endless meetings with government people...he was always having to start all over again. There were committees after committees, and I was on some of them, so I know. I couldn't understand how my husband could keep his cool for so long...you would be surprised how patient he was; I mean, he surprised me. Every time there would be a new committee, they would be very against Gerry, and against everything that he stood for. After a few meetings, of course, it would be changed, because they could see that Gerry was not the miserable fellow that they were told he was. Then the government would set up another committee...they were determined to get him."

On the advice of his family and friends, Bull fired Bennet and hired the prestigious Washington law firm of Troy, Malin and Pottinger, to represent him in an attempt to get his sentence reduced or set aside. The firm assigned Stanley Pottinger, once an assistant U.S. attorney-general, Warren Dennis, and Hamilton Loeb to work with local counsel, Anthony Lamb. They appeared before Judge Holden five times, in the month of July. According to documents they submitted, Bull had entered the Silver Hill Clinic, a private psychiatric hospital in New Canaan, Connecticut, on July 17, and was under twenty-four-hour guard, to prevent him from committing suicide.

Rodgers Gregory did not participate in this effort. He accepted his fate with resignation and, some say, a sense of relief, since he could at last see an end to years of agonizing indecision. He did not fight back, or try to change his plea. As scheduled, he began serving his sentence in Pennsylvania's Allenwood Correctional Institute on July 30.

Judge Holden refused to reduce or set aside Bull's sentence. On July 24, he also refused to recommend to the U.S. Bureau of Prisons that Bull be allowed to serve the six-month term in a Canadian mental hospital or prison, under a reciprocal agreement between the two countries. He did delay Bull's day of imprisonment to August 30, provided he remained at the Silver Hill Clinic until that date.

Coincident with Bull's American court appearances, the Canadian government finally took legal action against SRC-Québec. On March 8, 1980, *The Globe and Mail* reported that Rejean Paul, the justice department's regional director for Québec, had advised SRC officials that charges would be filed against Bull and the company. The same month, Bull agreed to an R.C.M.P. request that he take a lie-detector test, saying that he had nothing to hide. SRC's Canadian lawyers put a stop to that, and the legal maneuvers began.

Some idea of the sensitivity surrounding the case can be seen in the justice ministry's use of a rare legal procedure, under Section 455.3 of the Canadian Criminal Code, which allowed the judge to hear the evidence in secret, and gave him the power to order that the resulting transcripts not be placed in the public record.

R.C.M.P. and justice ministry spokesmen referred to the case's importance and "great complexity," and made strange references to their Star Chamber proceedings resulting "in a public airing of the facts." Just what the evidence was against Bull, who was involved, and the question of Canadian government complicity or acquiescence in the South African arms transfer, is still not known. While the hearings dragged on for months, SRC's lawyer, Garbriel LaPointe, issued a plea of guilty to all charges on the company's behalf, on August 14, 1980. Judge Rheal Brunet fined SRC $55,000, and the case was closed.

In Vermont, the desperate legal maneuvering continued. Bull gained another stay of execution of his sentence and, on September 24, his lawyers filed a "motion to set aside judgment of conviction to permit a withdrawal of a plea of guilty." While it would take until April 30, 1981, for his attorneys to finally give up on this motion, Bull was in jail long before that. Judge Holden, growing weary of the delays, told Bull to turn himself over to the authorities on October 1. A last-ditch appeal of his ruling, to the Second U.S. Circuit Court of Appeals, failed to produce a stay.

During his hospitalization at Silver Hills, where he was under the care of psychiatrist Dr. Robert Humphries, Bull regained, if not his heart, then at least his equilibrium. Unpleasant as it was, he slowly came to accept the fact that he had to go to jail. The press pictures of the time no longer showed rage or anger. A washed-out, apathetic face, calm only with the stillness of some deep exhaustion, looks back at the cameras without caring.

On a cold winter morning, with grey clouds hanging low over the foothills of the Appalachian mountains, Gerry Bull waved goodbye to Mimi and Charlie Murphy, who had driven him down from Connecticut, and walked through the gates of the Allenwood Federal Correctional Facility.

Many reports of Bull's imprisonment have called Allenwood, "a country-club jail," and indeed, it is actually next door to a private golf club. There are no fences or armed guards, and anyone who wanted to walk away from the place, could. In 1980, this minimum-security institution, for first-time, mainly white-collar offenders, housed some three hundred inmates. A collection of dormitories and low brick buildings on a thousand acres of rolling, partially forested land, it had a well-equipped gymnasium and even tennis courts, for prisoner recreation.

This picture ignores the old adage that iron bars do not a prison make, and the deep-seated feelings of humiliation that Bull endured. When he was taken into the reception area, he was fingerprinted, his were clothes taken away and, naked, he stood and spread his buttocks for inspection for possible contraband, by a guard with rubber gloves. A trustee stood ready to spray his groin with insecticide, should he answer *yes* to the query about body lice. His personal possessions, wallet, watch and rings were taken away and put into a storage envelope.

For the first time in his life, Gerry Bull had no claim to being special, powerful or better. He was just a number among many other numbers. A comfortable cage it might be, but he was still in jail.

THE RHINO SCAM

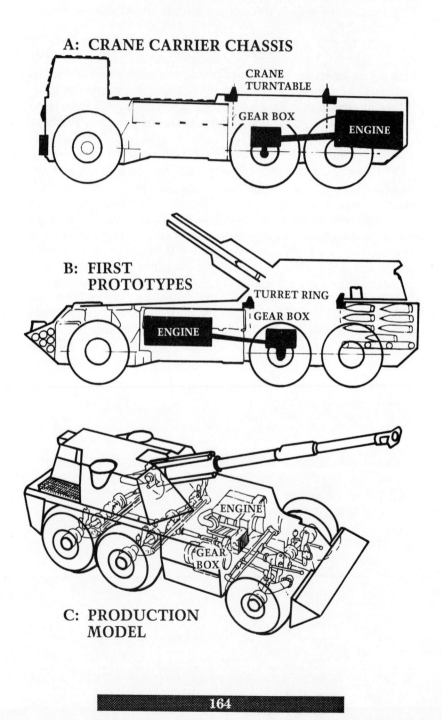

A: CRANE CARRIER CHASSIS

CRANE TURNTABLE

GEAR BOX

ENGINE

B: FIRST PROTOTYPES

TURRET RING

GEAR BOX

ENGINE

C: PRODUCTION MODEL

ENGINE

GEAR BOX

CHAPTER 15

But you feel betrayed?

Very much. I feel it's an overwhelming betrayal. What I did and what I built; to see it cheapened, to see people trying to degrade me personally, as a common criminal. For what?

—Gerry Bull and *W5*,
March 22, 1981

According to Mimi Bull, Gerry accepted his incarceration with "good grace." Perhaps because of his being a mechanical engineer, he was assigned a job in the prison's heating plant. He further occupied himself by researching the history of an old graveyard on the prison site, and by helping a fellow-inmate to write a story about the man's career.

Mimi visited him every week that he was in prison. Sometimes she came alone, other times in the company of the children. She says he bore up well, and was always glad to see her, even though she was often forced to be the bearer of bad news.

For, while Bull waited out his sentence in Allenwood, the little industrial empire he had kept alive through a decade of desperate expedient and sleight of hand, finally, irrevocably collapsed. SRC (U.S.), which had been renamed Saber Industries the year before, in a futile attempt to separate the electronics and air-traffic-control-simulator business from what Rodgers Gregory described as "the growing cancer" of the arms scandal, passed into receivership and dissolution, the month before Bull entered prison. On the Canadian side, there was an effort on the part of the government to keep at least parts of CTI alive, and to somehow hold on to Bull's acknowledged genius. The civil servants and the military bureaucrats at DND saw SRC-Q and its associated companies "as a key component of the Canadian munitions industry," whose continued operation was an "urgent requirement." Major General Ernest Creber, the associate assistant deputy minister of defense for material, told *The Globe and Mail* of March 11, 1980, that "there was no doubt other countries would like to recruit Dr. Bull," and that "such a move [would be] a serious loss to Canada."

But the political reality was that they had to get rid of Gerry Bull and the South African investment, before they could lend the companies money, or give them further contracts. Various schemes were floated, in which he would become an employee of the company while relinquishing ownership. The paradox was that SRC, without Bull in charge, was just a name and, at heart, the government knew it. Since they could not have their cake and eat it too, the decision was made to remove him from control of the companies, whether he could come up with the investment required to maintain them or not.

Since Bull was in prison, the weight of defending the companies against the government fell largely on Mimi's shoulders. She still remembers with bitterness the seizure of Valleyfield Chemical Products, a maneuver some of Bull's old co-workers have described as being done with "indecent haste." She said that "Valleyfield was doing very well, they had no reason [to seize it], they insisted that...he should find another partner to put more working capital in. We worked very hard to do that, and we had a written statement, saying that we had found a partner who had agreed to put a million and a half in it...so we told Ottawa, and they seized it the next day. They seized it on the twenty-fourth of December, which made it impossible to come up with the cash in the bank. It was unbelievable, because I can't believe any civil servant working overnight on the twenty-third of December, just to put that seizure in the next morning."

Expro Chemical Products Inc., the firm that now owns the Valleyfield munitions plant, purchased the facility in 1982 from the receivers, in a deal that was backdated to December of 1981. A corporate historical profile describes the incident with one terse line. "In December, Trust General, [the financial institution through which the government guaranteed loans to Valleyfield] had to take possession of the business, through its agent, Price Waterhouse Ltd.."

The transfer of the Thai order, via CCC, to Voest-Alpine, went through at the same time and, since SRC-Q had gone into receivership, the Austrians got the GC-45 technology free and clear, for their down payment of just $2 million. Asked if CCC took the operation out of the Bull family's hands completely, Mimi responded, "Yes, it was sold with their signature. They even had a celebration the night that Gerry was forced to sell the technology to Voest-Alpine. I couldn't believe it...I don't understand how they could celebrate that."

Shefford Electronics fared no better. Two years previously, through CCC, it had undertaken a contract to provide radio direction-finding equipment to the government of Kenya. Partially due to the client changing specifications in mid-stream, the project experienced severe cost overruns. As Michael Bull recalls, "The shortfall that the company experienced, to finish off that contract...was $1.7 million. We went to the government and said we needed some help. Now, the Kenyans had always been kept informed about it, and they were willing to increase the contract size by $1 million. Therefore, the shortfall became only $0.7 million, to finish off the contract. And we were saying to the government, 'Can you help us out; can you help us secure a subsidy, or at least a loan.'

"What they did is, they forced us out; they again seized the shares. They then turned around and gave the contract and the shares to Telefunken [A major German electronics firm]. They renegotiated the contract, and the contract was somewhere between $4 and $5 million to finish. Telefunken just proceeded on, with the same personnel, to finish off the contract, and then they closed down the company. Telefunken's interest in it was mainly the technology...they closed it down, and took the technology back to Germany."

Asked about his father's belief that the government was out to get him, Michael replied, "My father was absolutely correct. The actions against SRC-Q, Valleyfield and Shefford, all done in parallel, showed their determination to destroy this man."

If that was the intention, the ministers and bureaucrats in Ottawa were sadly mistaken. The Gerry Bull who walked out of Allenwood, in the bitterly cold hours before dawn, on February 13, 1981, might not have been the same man who went in, but he was anything but beaten. Charlie Murphy, as well as Mimi Bull and their five younger children, were waiting for him at the prison gate.

Bull did not return to Canada. Indeed, he would not see the land of his birth again for several years. According to Mimi, she, Gerry and the kids went to New York, where they spent several days, and then flew to the Franco-Dutch island of Saint-Martin, in the Caribbean, for several weeks of rest. Mimi says Gerry didn't feel comfortable about returning to Canada, and she implied that he feared the government might have something else up its sleeve. "He didn't know what to expect when he got here. He was fooled once, and he didn't want to get fooled again."

Also waiting for Bull, when he emerged from Allenwood, were a half-dozen journalists. One of them was veteran newsman Jim Reed, of CTV's *W5*. He remembers that, while Mimi and the family were happy and smiling, "Gerry was lost. He was very quiet...he seemed preoccupied, and wouldn't say anything much." Refusing to be put off, Reed and his camera crew followed the Bull's to a truck stop, where the family had breakfast. There, Bull told Reed that he just wanted to get out of North America, and that if he wanted to hear his side of the story, he should come and visit him later.

Reed accepted Bull's offer and, early in March, *W5* sent a crew to the Caribbean. Of the hundreds of interviews he has conducted over the years, Reed remembers his talk with Bull as one of the most interesting. "He was a fascinating person to talk to, or should I say listen to. He certainly dominated the conversation."

One of the reasons Bull agreed to talk to *W5* was that Reed had decided not to do an investigative piece. "We did our interview in two or three parts...our decision was basically to let Gerry Bull tell his side of the story. He seemed to be overjoyed that somebody was willing to listen to him talk about his ordeal. He wanted desperately to get his side of the story on the record. We told him that what we put on the air will clearly reflect what you tell us.

"He told me he thought there was a program of disinformation that had started in an orchestrated kind of way, almost simultaneously with his arrest. He said that people he'd been on good terms with suddenly turned on him, and he felt that it was orchestrated. He felt that this was part of a game plan to break him, to get him to admit guilt. In a way, he regretted not fighting his case, and in a way he didn't. He said that he could have fought it. He believed quite strongly he could have fought the whole thing in court. But it would have cost him several million dollars, and he couldn't afford it—either the time or the money involved. He said he was told by the justice department that, if he pleaded guilty, he would get a short time in jail, and that would be it, that they would not bother him again.

"After we finished the interview, our crew left, but I stayed on for a couple of days, and I spent some time just personally and privately with Mr. and Mrs. Bull. We went out for dinner a couple of times. I had to force him to let me pay the bill for one of those dinners. The other one he insisted. I was paying with a credit card, and he paid with cash. He had a large bundle, which he pulled out of his pocket and peeled off enough to pay the check.

"He said, 'I never believe in those things,' and he was looking at my credit card with some disdain. 'First of all, they take away any element of self-discipline you might have. Secondly, I don't like signing my name; you're always signing your name with those damn things.' He seemed to regard a VISA bill as a document that somebody was going to store away somewhere."

One thing attracted Reed's curiosity. "Gerry always carried a briefcase with him, in which I assumed were papers and notes and so forth...he never let this briefcase out of his sight, and if he didn't have it, Mimi had it. I found myself wondering what could be so important that he had to take it with him to the beach."

As to his future plans, Reed found Bull explicit, if only in a negative sense. "He told me that he was finished with North America, that he would have no further activities on this continent...other than that he hoped he could one day prove that he had been betrayed. As far as I can tell, he honestly believed he was innocent of any wrongdoing. He said everything he did had been cleared with whatever authorities were appropriate."

Yet, on certain points, Reed found him less than forthright. It was a strange mixture of candor and obscuration. "He would not discuss his contacts with South Africa. He never denied that he had them, but he wouldn't talk about them in detail, or name names.

"He said he was out of funds...and that he needed to rebuild his bank accounts. He didn't want to accept more money from his wife, or from the family. His indication to me was that his financial position was precarious. It was clear, however, that he had some support from somewhere, because he had plenty of money with which to travel to the Caribbean, or to Europe.

"He said that he would work for anyone...he felt he had been ideologically pure, in terms of being committed to free enterprise, to Canadian and American international goals...but that had changed...now he would have no qualms about working for the Soviet Union, or for China. He said his scientific work was all that was important now to him, and a goal...his goal was to bring the HARP program back to life. He still seemed preoccupied with HARP, he held the Canadian government responsible for its demise. He certainly had the intention of continuing with that work. It no longer mattered to him who financed it."

Asked how Bull struck him at the time, or if he showed any signs of strain, Reed said, "He didn't seem like anybody who'd been persecuted, he seemed very self-confident by the time he got to Saint-Martin. He was in pretty good shape; he was strong. He was angry, but he seemed together."

While many in Canada saw Bull as a finished, discredited man, whose career was over, Reed sensed the truth. That same month, he would finish his broadcast by telling the TV audience, "And if we think we've heard the last of Dr. Gerald Bull, this Canadian in exile; we haven't."

There is one loose end of the ARMSCOR affair that has puzzled arms analysts for nearly a decade, and which defies an exact place in the Bull chronology. It has to do with the origins of the South African self-propelled version of the GC-45 cannon, the G-6 Rhino.

Soviet and Western self-propelled (SP) guns are all slow, tank-like vehicles, designed to fight with armored divisions over the short distances of a hypothetical European war. Indeed, until a short time ago, the G-6 Rhino, with the technical exception of a very different, and much smaller, Czechoslovakian vehicle, was the only wheeled SP gun in the world. As such, it attracted much attention from defense specialists for its novelty value alone.

ARMSCOR was more than willing to satisfy their curiosity. Even in its early development stages, many pictures of the vehicle were released to world defense publications, and a prototype was prominently displayed at the Greek Arms Show, Defendory 82.

In both the international defense media, and on TV at home, the Rhino was held up as a shining example of South African ingenuity and the Afrikaner "can-do" mentality. They boasted about how this weapon-carrier is optimized to their unique requirements for strategic mobility, over distances of hundreds of kilometers. Since guerrilla-planted land mines were deemed a particular threat, the front hull is V-shaped, and equipped with blow-out plates to channel the force of a blast away from the isolated driver's compartment, just aft of the bush plow.

To make a pun, it's all Bull; or, if one prefers, a classic example of disinformation at work. An unknown writer for *Jane's Defence Weekly* almost caught it in 1984, when he wondered why South Africa was trying so hard to market a vehicle so specialized that few, if any, nations would want it.

As mentioned in Chapter 10, the Canadian army's Directorate of Land Requirements (DRL) had a competition for a self-propelled gun, in the mid and late seventies. Bull's proposal was very similar to the Rhino and, while only a scale-model and design presentation, it used the same six-wheel, 21 X 25 tire arrangement as the Rhino. It was designated the HMSP, for High Mobility, Self-Propelled gun.

During a discussion of Bull's South African involvement, three years ago, a colleague of mine remembered an old magazine article that referred to a possible Canadian content for the Rhino. "I'll dig it out and send it over to you," he said. "Who knows, you might find something interesting."

Indeed. There, in the December 1982 issue of *International Defence Review* was this comment, in a photo caption. "Using the same basic barrel and oscillating mechanism as the G-5 towed howitzer, the ARMSCOR G-6 self-propelled gun...is based on a six-wheeled Canadian off-road vehicle chassis."

Now *based* is an elastic word, and can be taken to mean a design copy which, to the technically inclined, would be interesting, but hardly dramatic. Then there were these oblique references, in the January 1983 issue of *MILITARY TECHNOLOGY* magazine. "Development of the G-6 is almost complete. The prototype[s] so far built still use a certain amount of foreign-manufactured components purchased through normal commercial channels, as they are not considered as defence-related items and consequently do not fall under the UN embargo."

Canadian parts in the Rhino? Based on a twenty-year record of South Africa using Canada as a spare-parts depot for military tank and truck components, it seemed a reasonable surmise.

George MacDonald is head of the heavy-duty equipment-repair course at Sheridan College, in Mississauga, Ontario. He has had three decades of engineering experience with machinery like the Rhino. Presented with a sheaf of Rhino technical drawings, taken from publications such as *Jane's* and *International Defence Review*, he quickly identified major parts, such as the gearbox, turret ring, axles and suspension, by make and model number.

"Not that that's going to do you much good," he said. "There's a thousand places where you could buy those components." To explain, MacDonald sketched the nature of the industry that produces such machines. In spite of their size, the companies that build them are usually quite small. Others have described it as a "cottage industry," where the builder, or integrator, as they are known, takes standardized components made by others, and assembles them on a small number of purpose-built chassis, for a wide variety of purposes. It is a Meccano-set approach, where the prime determinant to component selection is the wheel size.

As the conversation was coming to an end, MacDonald picked up one of the Rhino photos again. "You know, that's really odd," he said, tapping a picture of the prototype with his pencil. "That 21 x 25 wheel arrangement...I don't believe there's been anything like that built since the early fifties. It's obsolete, eh." Asked what type of vehicle might have used such an arrangement, MacDonald said, "Well, way back, there was a crane-carrier that looked like that," and he named a company that produces a well-known brand of such equipment.

This information led to an astonishing discovery. The Rhino was not *based* on a six-wheeled Canadian off-road vehicle chassis; *it was one*. For the Rhinos, or at least the first nine of them, are not new vehicles at all, but rebuilt scrap, a metamorphosis of that ancient, heavy-duty mobile crane-carrier that MacDonald referred to.

The idea that this ferocious South African weapon of war once motored the peaceful highways of Canada, on it's way to remote construction sites, began with an analysis of military-press reports on the Rhino's development. Here was a story of puzzling production delays and inexplicable design blunders.

The first Rhino prototype was unveiled by South Africa in 1981, and it was confidently announced that series production would begin at Lyttleton Engineering Works by 1983, at the latest. This did not happen, and it soon became evident that the vehicle was deficient in a number of ways. Its rocking-beam rear suspension could not stand up to the high-speed pounding of rutted gravel roads, and the sidewalls of the tires themselves were not strong enough to take the flexing imposed by rough terrain.

Macdonald found this a curious error for a designer working on a new vehicle to make, since the load and stress factors are easy to calculate. Here, the divergence between the source vehicle and the Rhino requirements began showing up. According to tire specialists, the tread and sidewall design of the 21 x 25 tire, shown on the first Rhino prototype, is specifically designed for cruising on paved highways and then crawling over rough terrain. Like the source vehicle, the rocking-beam suspension is only suitable for high-speed travel on smooth roads. Several other engineering details link the two machines, but the most curious failure of the initial Rhino had to do with the gun. It could not elevate more than halfway to its maximum firing position, because the loading tray hit the gear box, which was between the middle pair of wheels. Since anyone with a compass could have calculated that, it became a prime clue to the Rhino's *ad hoc* origins.

Even if it was initially a failure, the adaptation is a brilliant piece of improvisation that has all the hallmarks of a Gerry Bull idea. The sheer ball turntable that supported the crane became the turret ring of the gun housing. Since the stresses imposed by a crane load and the firing of the gun occur in the same planes and angles, no modification to the technically difficult-to-produce turret ring was required.

The drawing on page 164 shows the evolution of the Rhino from crane carrier to the final successful design, which only reached the South African Army units in Angola in 1988, five years later than initially projected. Note how the engine and drive shaft were rotated 180 degrees forward on the chassis, to clear the rear compartment for crew space and ammunition storage. Unfortunately, this still left the transmission over the middle pair of wheels. The final solution moved the transmission forward into the engine compartment, and connected it to the drive train through a device known as a drop box. With all-wheel drive, shock-absorber pneumatic suspension and stronger tires, the Rhino was finally a workable weapon.

Where is the proof of the Canadian link? The very age of the design allowed the record of the crane-carrier shipments to South Africa to be discovered. The engineering description of the Rhino chassis is an "integrated wagon mount, close coupled rear end," and it only applies to a 21 X 25 wheel arrangement. As such, it has a Canadian International Trade Classification (CITC) code number of 513-15-52. This numbering system is used by Statistics Canada (STATSCAN) to compile a data base of exports, by commodities, to various nations.

To protect "manufacture confidentiality," the data base cuts the last two figures from the publicly-available indexes, relegating it to a group of some thirteen crane-related products. However, a source in a Canadian government tax department has confirmed that the suspected manufacturer applied for use of the full number, at the relevant times.

First instituted in 1963, the data-base references, for trade to South Africa, of CITC number 513-15 are blank until April of 1980. Commencing that month, and continuing until December, Canada exported one such product a month to South Africa, for a total of nine units. In February of 1981, South Africa revealed the first Rhino prototype.

Equally significant in the Rhino story is CITC code number 513-98. It covers parts and components applicable to crane-related vehicles. From 1980 to 1987, they form a pattern whose peaks in dollar value precede each benchmark in the Rhino development chronology.

In February 1984, South Africa unveiled the first ADV (Advanced Development Vehicle) model of the Rhino, following the previous year's surge of parts shipments. (the declared cash value of the 1983 shipments totals $1,039,000.) The next year, commencing in February and ending in December, Canada exported eleven more 513-15 units to South Africa, for a total of twenty units. After that, part shipments fall to zero, until late 1986. In 1987, when Lyttleton Engineering produced four Engineering Development Rhinos that contained all the changes to be introduced into the production model, a final burst of components is registered, then the record drops to zero. In early 1988, ARMSCOR announced that series production of the Rhino had commenced. Curiously, military commentators like John Reed estimate that South Africa has deployed "around twenty" of these vehicles.

The hard, documentary proof to connect Bull and the Canadian subsidiary of the company suspected of producing and/or modifying the crane-carrier chassis for South Africa, has not yet surfaced. But corporate financial statements for the companies involved in the sale of the license production rights for this brand of crane-carrier, between 1978 and 1980, reveal a curious fact. In preparation for the sale, the vendor planned to dispose of a number of crane-carriers it had maintained as a rental fleet. This was done at write-off prices, since the value of the equipment, after being depreciated at 6.6 percent per annum, had declined to virtually zero.

Proof does exist that SRC-International had a HMSP project under-way long after the GC-45 transfer to South Africa was judged finished. In the SRC-International documents obtained from the Voest-Alpine trial, the board of directors' minutes for October 5, 1979, makes clear that one GC-45-related project, entitled "HMSP" was exempt from the arrangement to transfer the GC-45 technology to Voest-Alpine. After discussing the writedown of SRC-I's debts to SRC-Q, the document states, "The passing of the present resolution will also cancel a resolution passed by the Board of Directors on April 1st, 1978, which made SRC-Q the privileged supplier of SRC-I for all ERA (Extended Range Ammunition) products, the GC 39/45 ordnance system, the H.M.S.P. as regards SRC-I territories until further notice. This condition was specifically agreed by Dr. G.V. Bull, President of SRC-Q."

On November 19, 1979, the technology transfer-agreement between Voest-Alpine, SRC-I, SRC-Q and PRB again mentions the HMSP. Under the heading, GRANT OF LICENSE, section 1.2 reads as follows:

> The license under Section 1.1 does not include a license for the manufacture and sale in the Licensed Territories of the "HMSP" application of the Licensed Products (under "HMSP" is understood a particular product development in which SRC-I is already involved.)

While the conversion idea has all the slapdash brilliance of a Bull brainstorm, any direct connection with the Rhino scam was probably minimal, after the initial stages. The removal of SRC-Q from its role as "privileged supplier" was certainly a security move, to distance the source companies from the ARMSCOR scandal. SRC-I, or some other specially-created front organization, could have easily handled the coordination of the parts and chassis orders.

It would take until 1988, and an arms show in Baghdad, for the world to be reminded of whose idea the Rhino really was, and where South Africa's "can-do mentality" really came from.

CHAPTER 16

On September 22, 1980, eight days before
Gerry Bull entered Allenwood prison,
the then-obscure Middle East nation of
Iraq launched a sudden attack on its neighbor, Iran. That it was the start of the first
major war in centuries, which did not directly involve the interests of European nations
or the philosophies they spawned, was in
no way apparent. Six army divisions, comprising seventy thousand men and two thousand Soviet tanks, crossed the confluence
of the Tigris and Euphrates rivers, north
of the Persian Gulf. Streaming across pon-
toon roadways that bridged kilometers of
swamps, mud flats and river channels, they
drove up to eighty kilometers into the popu-
lous and oil-rich Iranian province of
Khuzestan.

While a long-standing border dispute,
over control of the strategic Shatt al Arab
waterway, was the reason given for the
unprovoked assault, the strategic objectives
of Iraqi leader Saddam Hussein were both
simple and brutal. He calculated that an
Iranian military defeat would topple the
shaky theocracy of Ayatollah Khomeni, and
dramatically shift the balance of Mid East
power in Iraq's favor.

All went well, at first. The Iranian army was demoralized, and its professional officer corps had been purged by the Islamic revolution. Caught by surprise, many of their best remaining units were crushed by the sheer mass of the Iraqi assault. Hundreds of modern tanks and guns, which the deposed Shah had purchased from Western nations, were lost. Yet Iran did not collapse, as Saddam Hussein thought it would. A Machiavellian cynic, he could not comprehend the moral force that the Iranian revolution had called forth in a hitherto despised and oppressed nation.

While the initial Iraqi assault broke through to the northeast, across the plains of Khuzestan, to threaten the vital communications centre of Dezful, the city of Khorramshahr and the oil port of Abbadan were invested, but not immediately taken. Because the river and the swamps directly to its west cut it off from direct links with the home-land, the Iraqi invasion force was actually in a salient, open to attack from the east, while its main supply line ran north-south, back to the original crossing points. Logistics problems, inexperience in conducting large-scale military operations, and bungling Iraqi generals who allowed trapped Iranian tank formations to escape, soon brought the advance to a permanent halt.

Where Saddam had expected a blitzkrieg victory, and a quick peace that would give Iraq the territory he felt it needed to secure access to the Persian Gulf, he now had a war with no definable end. Conquering the vast and mountain-riven expanses of Iran beyond Khuzestan was out of the question. Retreat, with its loss of prestige, was also not an option. But, as wrong as he had been on the course of the war and its results, Saddam's judgment of how America, the USSR and the nations of Western Europe would react to his aggression, was remarkably accurate.

Iraq's attack was universally denounced by the world community. The Russians even went so far as to embargo further weapons and spare-parts shipments to an army and air force that were overwhelmingly Soviet-based. But, when the Kremlin's clumsy attempts to profit from the political situation in Iran fizzled, the policy was reversed six months later. Economics also played a role in the Soviet decision. The multi-billion dollar flow of hard currency from weapons sales to Iraq was sorely missed by the basket-case Soviet economy, and the war promised even greater profits. With the exception of certain requested items that the Soviet army regarded as "home-front technology," the shipments were resumed on a vastly greater scale. Either by direct airlift from the Soviet Union, or by ship through the Jordanian port of Aqaba, millions of tons of the Soviet Union's latest weaponry helped to bolster Iraqi resistance.

America, still smarting from the humiliation of the Teheran hostage crisis, took a well-disguised pleasure at the event and, over the coming years, would take a number of steps to aid Saddam. One was to provide Iraq with satellite intelligence data on Iranian military dispositions; another was to lend its assistance in assuring that Iraq got the loans it needed from the world banking community, to pay for its Soviet tanks, guns and aircraft.

The reaction of European nations toward the Iraq-Iran war was a curious mixture of historical sentimentality and cold-eyed calculation. With their visceral memories of the Great Jihad, which had swept the Muslim faith to the Pyrenees and the gates of Vienna half a millennium before, they saw an attack on Iran as anything but a cause for concern, no matter what their public pronouncements might say. Iranian leaders, who talked about stopping their revolution on the Atlantic Ocean, and made statements about how "all Europe will soon be Muslim," helped fuel the perception. Even better, there were vast amounts of money to be made, trading military hardware and technological-infrastructure development contracts for oil.

Britain, perhaps because of its long experience of playing colonial master in the Persian Gulf region, was initially reticent to feed the Iraqi military machine. But, as the conflict grew in size and intensity, the Thatcher government was besieged by businessmen, who correctly pointed out that a dozen European nations were reaping rich harvests from the war. Slowly, the position shifted to one of benign tolerance for business with Iraq that did not directly involve supplying arms. The considerable expertise of British construction and engineering firms was to be turned to tasks like building airfields, army bases and other infrastructure projects.

Iraq had learned several lessons from its previous experiences with Soviet arms embargoes, especially the 1960s cut-off, over President al Bakr's threats against Kuwait. In the long term, they set about trying to acquire as much indigenous military production capability as possible. In the tactical sense, they learned to stockpile spare parts, and they went looking for a wider range of weapons and suppliers.

Even before the war with Iran began, the Iraqi army was undergoing a rapid expansion, from a mere infantry force to a more modern, armored strike force. But, even with its growth plans fueled by some $20 billion a year in oil revenues, Iraq could not do everything at once. U.S. defense analyst John Wagner, writing a C.I.A.-cleared article for the 1982 edition of *Fighting Armies*, stated, "The Iraqi army is seriously deficient in artillery firepower...compared with other major armed forces in the Middle East. Since 1979, their army has been striving to improve its artillery forces." He later pointed out that they could be expected to turn to the Soviet Union and Western Europe for new and more powerful guns.

The battles in Khuzestan, and the renaissance of Iranian martial vigor, were back-page items in the newspapers that Bull must have read in Allenwood, yet we can be sure he took an interest. The beleaguered Iraqi invaders were being hit by ever-growing Iranian counterattacks, by the time Gerry was sunning himself on Caribbean beaches.

Mimi Bull's hope that Gerry's sojourn in Saint-Martin would provide him with a period of rest and reflection was only half fulfilled. As they walked the beaches of Saint-Martin together, Jim Reed recalled that Bull would often stop and stare fixedly at the horizon for long minutes, without speaking. Reflection there might be, but there was no rest. Many of Bull's male friends and associates have said that Bull's imprisonment did not seem to affect him that much. As Charlie Murphy put it, "He was the same Gerry. I didn't notice any change in his personality at all."

Mimi Bull had a slightly different opinion. When asked what effects her husband's imprisonment had on him, this normally articulate and quick-witted woman went silent for a long time. "Yes," she finally answered, "I think he was more...I won't say withdrawn, but more...reflective, perhaps. He was concerned with all the problems that had arisen...there was a weight there."

Gerry Bull never lived in Canada again and, unlike his son Michael, he did not move his family to Europe when Brussels later became their headquarters. His travail seems to have caused a subtle and permanent shift in his attitudes toward his wife and family. There is no question that he felt humiliated by his experiences, and Jim Reed is not the only person to have noticed that Bull found taking money from his wife's family a distasteful necessity. It is an all-too-human characteristic for a recipient of favors to develop a perverse feeling about those who feed him. This is not to claim that Bull came to dislike his family. Feelings of shame can isolate a person more easily from those they care for, than from those they do not.

Mimi agreed that their time together was less after Gerry left Saint-Martin. Although she said that, in the following decade, "I used to go about three or four times a year to Europe. I always saw him then," that can hardly be considered a life together.

But it must be remembered that Mimi had her own good reasons for remaining in Canada and, being a strong personality, was not merely an extension of Gerry Bull. The Bulls' three youngest children, Robert, Kathleen and Noemi Jane, were still in high school. There were also the houses in Montréal and Highwater to manage, along with the truncated piece of land around Highwater that the Bulls had kept from the creditors.

Reports vary on what Bull did after he left Saint-Martin. According to Mimi, "He went to Paris for several months, then to London for several months." While recent news stories have listed various exotic destinations for Bull, and even claimed he had clandestine meetings with the head of a now-famous Middle East nation, Mimi is correct. Simply because he wasn't traveling that much, Bull's whereabouts, for the six months after his release, are quite traceable. As his new business partner would later explain, Bull had urgent reasons for his European destinations.

Asked when he first became involved in his father's business affairs, Michael Bull replied, "It was late '81 when I started, but I actually joined, full time, in '82."

Right from the beginning, the new relationship between the two previously-estranged men was a paradoxical one. On the one hand, it was confused and often confrontational; on the other, it was to prove a remarkably successful match of talents and skills. It is no slur on Michael to say he defines their personal and business relationship in contradictory terms. There is no other way he can describe it. In one way, they were equals, in another, Michael was very much the subordinate. Even on the question of who first came up with idea of him joining his father's endeavors, Michael says he can't honestly answer. "It was sort of half and half...we gave signals to one another...we edged around it...he wanted me to join at that very time because he was afraid of the financial future."

Michael then went on to refer to a letter his father wrote to him in 1981. Nothing so illustrates the suppressed emotionalism of the two men's relationship as its contents, which Michael only discovered after his father's death. "You can watch these movies where the father tells the son he loves him," he said, "and then the son turns around and says 'I love you too, Dad.' But in real life, that's not the way it actually goes. There's a sort of subtle awkwardness that comes into play. The letter basically says, 'I've gone through hell, and I've discovered what it means to have my son standing beside me.' He never sent it to me."

Asked if he put any conditions on his involvement, Michael replied, "No, not really. In 1981, he was a very bitter man, and he had a lot of agressivity [sic] in him. Which is understandable. I'm making a metaphor here, but if it was cloudy outside, he would say, 'What a shitty day, it's raining.' If you said 'Well, it's cloudy, but its not really raining,' he would go and throw a tantrum. So there was no firm agreement or anything there. We sort of agreed that I would take over the finance and administration, and look at the contractual things, but, you know, we worked more in terms of a partnership; he was the boss, but I was his associate. Call him a managing partner. I'm not throwing myself any flowers...because he was the boss. I was promoted, and I'm using that term very liberally, to general manager in 1984, which is two and a half years afterwards."

Comparing their characters, Michael said, "There was no stop to his belief in himself, to his capabilities. I was very pragmatic, very down to earth. He was the dreamer, and I was more or less the operator. He was a terrific marketer, too much so, because he tended to oversell. I was the guy who was stuck with the problems. The one thing, why we were successful, we couldn't get rid of one another; you just can't fire one another. Our fights never took on a personal nature, because they were professional fights."

For the twenty-five-year-old Michael Bull, his introduction to the armaments game was a savage one. He quickly saw the type of people his father was dealing with. Joseph Severin might be dead, but his style of operations lingered on at PRB. Bull still owned his forty-five percent interest in SRC-International, and there was to be yet another argument with his Belgian partners. As Michael described it, "After my dad got out of jail, he realized that PRB had taken the opportunity to screw us good. There was a contract with Jordan, which we all believe now, went to Iraq. But, legally speaking, the contract is with Jordan, and unless you go and call the Jordanians liars, that's where it went."

Asked about the nature of this transaction, Michael said, "It was a joint contract. Basically, the Jordanians were buying 200 guns from Voest-Alpine, and 225,000 rounds of ammunition from PRB. That is the famous contract that everyone now claims went directly from Jordan to Iraq. The agreement we had with SRC-I was that we here, SRC-Q, were to get a subcontract of part of the metal parts for the ammunition. You see, we did not have the facility to do the filling, or do the charge...now we were a small company, and we didn't need a big piece of the cake. That would have saved our butt."

Here, Michael dispelled a common assumption about the bankruptcy of SRC-Q. While it did go under in 1981, shortly before Gerry Bull went to jail, it was CTI, the Bulls' holding company, that put it into receivership. As Michael describes it, "CTI had previously lent SRC-Q over $5.5 million, in the form of a debenture. CTI put SRC-Q into default. The tactic being to try and protect it's assets from creditors." While this did not prevent Voest-Alpine from using the bankruptcy clause in its agreement with PRB and SRC-Q, it did isolate and preserve Bull's share in SRC-International.

Referring back to the Jordanian deal, Michael said, "The contract was signed somewhere in 1981, but it was well on the way in 1980. PRB strung my father along, and waited till CTI was no longer in a position to fight. Then it went in, signed the agreement, and took the whole contract for itself...We figured that the Space Research portion of it would have been somewhere in the order of $80 million. The final bankruptcy of CTI involved a total debt of around $9 million. This contract would have saved it. But PRB took it all, in a very greedy manner. So my father, when he saw that, he said, 'OK, these guys want to do that, fine.' Then PRB sent a message through the InterPost people saying 'We can't really mix with you, due to your reputation now. You've got a record.' Meanwhile, at the same time, they changed the specification of the shell. They were using now a cheaper and softer metal, and they were no longer welding the nubs [which engage the rifling in the barrel, and keep the shell straight] but machining them. It was a major change, especially the change in material specifications...we felt the shell would have to go through a qualification round again. But PRB cut the corners short; in fact, they used the changes to say that its not really your round that we sold."

As Michael later continued the story, "We're now up to late '81, and we've severed our contacts with PRB. PRB is spreading all types of rumors that INTERPOL is after my father. Then, finally, the contract between PRB and V-A and Jordan gets into trouble. There have been some poor testing and some failures and, of course, then they start to fight. PRB saying that the gun is no good. V-A turns around and says, 'No, its the ammunition.'"

Other sources have said that the problem was that the riding nubs would sometimes break off, causing the shell to jam in the barrel, which resulted in the gun blowing up. Michael would only describe the problem as, "catastrophic failures, period. Everybody was complaining, there were a lot of dispersion problems and whatnot. So, suddenly, there's a courtship going on again, trying to get my father back...We have a big meeting in Paris in 1982 between V-A, PRB and ourselves. My father is asked [at the instigation of V-A] to look into the matter. My dad, he was no angel...but he had one tremendous quality...he never bore a grudge, provided that the other party came in and slapped his back and said, 'OK, Gerry, let's forget the past and go on.' So he dropped all his grudges against V-A and PRB, and said, 'OK, I'll do that.' So we had a small contract, between twenty-five to thirty thousand dollars, as a consultancy figure...I remember telling my dad, 'That's outrageous; are PRB going to come in and say we have a moral obligation to get them some royalties?' My dad said, 'Maybe they will, I don't know.'

"A few weeks down the line, I couldn't bear it any longer, and I remember asking the Belgians, 'Look, you're asking us here to make a professional technical opinion; will you follow any recommendations we make?' They said, 'Well, no, not really.' I asked them 'Do you guys feel you owe us anything, have any moral obligations to us?' They said 'No, absolutely not.' I said, 'Very good.' I turned to my dad and said, 'There's no point talking to these assholes. Let's go.' And so relations were broken again.

"Meanwhile, we had settled down again in Belgium, because we needed a temporary home, and it turned out to be permanent. In the summer of '82, we finally decided to finalize the divorce from SRC-I. We got out of SRC-I altogether in October 1982, with the clear understanding they would change the name: my father was always very serious about keeping the name, SRC. I had no compunction, I said 'Why don't we call ourselves something else,' but, no, he would never hear of that. So PRB kept the name, but we had set up our own company in Belgium, called Space Research, SA. They went further and tried to sue us for using the name.

"Eventually, they changed their name to IOSS (International Ordnance Sales and Service), in 1985. They kept the name SRC-International for about three years or so, which led to a lot of confusion. Some of our Telexes ended up there, and we would get some of theirs. In Belgium, we were called Space Research Corp SA, they were called SRC-International SA. Meanwhile, we had other companies set up around Europe, in quite a number of countries. Using the letters, SRC, which led to a hell of a lot of confusion."

Michael says, "We received no recompense at all for that contract...none." Since the Austrian documentary evidence shows that V-A had no legal obligation to pay the Bulls anything for the Jordanian business, or any other, for that matter, it is a reasonable claim.

Why did the Bulls hang on to their connections with people who had treated them so shabbily? Michael implies that it was his father's financial straits. This raises the question of whether Gerry Bull was really as broke as he said. *Profil*, the Austrian news-magazine, whose coverage of the Bull story has been remarkably accurate, says he got out of the ARMSCOR affair with up to $6 million. Even if true, such a view misses a salient point. From an arms-business standpoint, $6 million is peanuts. For, what did Bull have to sell? When they started out in Brussels, the Bulls had no factories, no staff, not even a secretary. As Michael put it, "It was just me and my dad in those days, that was the company." From a business perspective, all that was left was Gerry's knowledge and research skills. Talents which, combined with his ability to invent and problem-solve, made him a unique resource.

Which helps explain why PRB and V-A would want to keep their connections with SRC. Wheelers and dealers that they were, they recognized the utility of Bull's technical brilliance, in solving the problems of them producing a product he had devised.

Consultancy is perhaps the most elastic term in the English language. It can cover such a wide range of activities. Knowledge may be viewed as a product, but it is a uniquely nebulous one, and almost impossible to trace. Asked if their business, at the time, took this track, Michael answered, "That's right. In '82...we had a few little contracts from PRB and V-A. Then we had a contract with China, quite a number of them. Succeeding contracts took us from '82 to '83 to '84, and onward. It developed into a fairly substantial work with China."

Asked if this was again consultancy work, Michael replied, "For '82, '83, that's correct. In '84 the contract took the format of a major technology transfer."

Strangely, the developer of the GC-45 was forced to turn to Voest-Alpine, in arranging the sale to China of his own technology. As Michael explains it, "With the bankruptcy, most of the documentation was destroyed. So we were left with the basic concept. Everybody thinks my father designed everything...but it was a corporate effort. We were left with trying to make business, and without all the data packages. In '83, '84, when we had the contracts with China, we were stuck. We had nothing to sell, really. They wanted to pay for drawings. Funny enough, we purchased them back from Voest-Alpine. [laughs] We purchased the technical data packages, because we no longer had the originals. I know we were at odds, but we still talked to them. At one point we helped them out...in late 1982, they were stuck with a production problem...a part kept failing, and they could not identify the problem. And as sort of a *quid pro quo* for helping them to solve the problem, they let us have the GHN drawing packages."

One of the quirks of Communist Chinese politics, in the early 1980s, was the privatization of many defense plants previously owned by the People's Liberation Army (PLA). One of these new firms was the huge China North Industries (NORINCO). Under the "four modernizations" program, this conglomerate, which may employ over four hundred thousand workers, was burdened with hundreds of out-of-date factories, slavishly copying early 1960s-era Soviet weaponry. They were desperately seeking new technology, both to equip their own forces and to provide hard currency through overseas arms sales.

This was to make NORINCO and the Bulls natural partners. It was also a deal that was to make the new SRC a great deal of money. Just how much is open to dispute, but Michael allows that it was a good deal. When it came to negotiating the contracts, he was an excellent bargainer, and he brought his accountancy skills to the task. In what he described as "quite a number of visits to China," he conducted "long, arduous negotiations with them," to make sure his impetuous father was not ripped off again.

It would take several years before NORINCO would offer the WAC-21, their clone of the GHN-45, on the world arms market, but the new, profit-oriented attitude of the NORINCO arms conglomerate would soon show up in massive sales of Bull's shells to Iran.

By late 1983, Iraq's military situation had become desperate, and most military commentators were predicting it would lose the war. Major Iranian offensives had hurled them out of Khuzestan, with the loss of over a hundred thousand men, and many tanks and guns. For Saddam Hussein was finding out just what sort of giant he had awakened. All over Iran, not only in the cities, but in thousands of villages a hard week's march from a paved road, hundreds of thousands of men and young boys heard the call of the mullahs to holy war.

Enlisted into the regular army, or the legions of the newly-formed Revolutionary Guard, these volunteers were hastily trained, armed with little more than rifles and hand grenades, and hurled against the invader. It was literally flesh against steel. Old men, and illiterate young boys with sticks, often went ahead of regular army units to detonate land mines. It was suicide, but it made holes in the Iraqi defences, through which the human waves behind them came pouring in. Call them fanatics, but they rose from their trenches with the doomed courage of the soldiers of World War I. "*Allu Akhbar!!* God is great!!" they cried, and charged the Iraqi bunkers and dug-in tanks. Machine guns, mortars and high-velocity tank guns sometimes stopped them, but there was always another wave, and many Iraqi units simply ran out of ammunition. Khorramshahr was retaken, and soon the only Iraqi soldiers in Khuzestan were either dead or in prison camps. By the end of 1983, the Iranian "Army of God," as they styled themselves, was pushing into Iraq, and the swamps and marshes of the Shat al Arab. Their stated objective was Baghdad, and the head of Saddam Hussein.

As their ancestors had done a thousand years before, the Iraqis turned to artillery, in an attempt to turn back the Persian hordes. More and more Iranian assaults were met by the peculiar moaning sound of Bull's extended range, 155mm shells coming in at them.

Long-range artillery is a terrible weapon against infantry in the open; no weapon the attacker carries can effectively duel with it, and no amount of faith or courage can make a difference. For the Iranians, their attacks against the port city of Basra turned into a series of bloodbaths, on the scale of World War I battles such as Verdun or the Somme. Often equipped with radar proximity fuses, the long-nosed shells burst in the air above the attacking hordes, scything them down with white-hot metal fragments. Time and again, when the Iraqi defensive systems buckled, it was artillery that sealed off the breeches and kept the positions intact.

While most of Iraq's cannon were Soviet guns, like the M-46 130mm guns that the GHN-45's South African brother, the G-5, fought in Angola, it was those two hundred Bull-designed guns that could reach further, with more accuracy and flexibility, than any other tube weapon in the Iraqi arsenal. So effective were they that the Iraqis decided they needed more. Strangely, the source for these new guns was not to be Voest-Alpine, which had now changed the name of its artillery production wing to NORICUM SA, but South Africa.

When they were delivered, and how many, are questions that get a variety of answers. Asked his thoughts on the matter, Michael Bull replied, "It's hard to know...we know there's a hundred South African guns in the Middle East. Our thoughts were originally that these went to Iran. Subsequently, that seems to be wrong, and they have gone to Iraq, which would make the total in Iraq at about three hundred...My guess is that the Iraqis got about two hundred from Austria and about a hundred from South Africa."

John Reed, the English-based defense journalist, has been a close follower of ARMSCOR's activities in the past decade. As he described it, "The original story was that South Africa supplied some guns to Iran...that was the original story, and then the story came out in South Africa, very strongly, that we are not supplying Iran...no way are we supplying anything more to Iran. We might have sold them some guns in the past but we're not going to tell you. They didn't say it officially, but they actually had diverted fifty guns from the South African army, to get swift delivery in 1985, or thereabouts, into Iraq. Then they built some more."

Reed believes the number of G-5s sent to Iraq may have been larger than that, and the delivery dates earlier. He points out that South Africa's shell production and powder industry certainly benefited from the war. According to him, SOMCHEN shipped over five thousand container-loads of G-5 propellant charges to Iraq during the war.

"There are two other pieces of information on this that lead me to believe that your original sources have misinformed you," Reed says. "One, I met Don Hemming, Sales Manager of ARMSCOR, in Turkey about eighteen months ago, and asked him, first of all, 'Have you supplied these guns to Iraq?' And he said, 'Yes, we've supplied them to Iraq,' and only then because I said I'd seen pictures of them there. Then, just recently, there was a question asked in the South African parliament as to whether the South Africans had received payment in full from Iraq for military equipment supplied. And the answer was yes, and that there were no outstanding credits, no outstanding debts from Iraq."

One possible reason for the Iraqis switching sources is that they found out that NORICUM had another customer for the GHN-45— Iran. In 1987, when I told Gerry Bull that I was planning to visit Iraq, he said, "Why do you want to visit those bastards for?" He then went on to praise the Iranian side, and stated he had visited the country several times. "The GC-45 is probably in bigger use in Iran; they have more than the Iraqis by now," he declared proudly. While this may have been mere dissimulation on Bull's part, his outstanding dislike of South Africa was made clear. "South Africa ripped me off," Bull said, and he referred to the G-5 as "a shoddy copy of my weapon." Perhaps the fact that ARMSCOR was doing business with Iraq displeased him.

MILITARY TECHNOLOGY magazine's *World Defense Almanac* for 1987-88 lists, under Iraqi artillery holdings, this bracketed comment. "Some 140 GHN-45 have been delivered, with an apparent order for 600, causing some concern in Austria." The next year, it states, "Some 500 GHN-45 have been delivered."

Michael Bull denies his father made several visits to Iran. He is not even sure if Bull actually went there. "I'm only aware of one possible trip. I'm not sure if he even made it. But, no, he did not go several times; I think he went over to visit. They asked him to come over, he went, he talked to them, and he came back. You know, there was nothing we could do with Iran."

Asked when the visit occurred, Michael said, "I don't know, somewhere around '87, I guess. I'm not even sure if he made it. On that particular aspect, he never came out and said what he wanted to say. I'm not sure if he met Iranians somewhere in the Middle East or Near East, such as Greece, for instance, or in Yugoslavia, or if they had actually met in Iran. I don't know."

One coincidence should be mentioned. In 1987, China began selling large amounts of weaponry to Iran, providing yet another breach in the American-led arms embargo. Copies of Soviet Mig-21 jet fighters are the most well-known examples, but China also began providing large quantities of artillery shells, specifically 155mm, though it cannot be definitely established if they were for Bull's guns, or standard shells for the considerable Iranian holdings of old American 155mm howitzers.

By 1987, SRC, according to Michael, was no longer doing business with China. "That contract was terminated in '87. At that time, we could see that the situation in China was reversing itself. The open-door policy was back to a hard-line policy." While it is true that China was blowing colder that year, for western businessmen in general, it is also possible that the technology transfers, and their hard-currency payments, were simply over. One thing is certain. By 1987, SRC was no longer two men in a Belgian office. It had grown far bigger and far richer than that.

CHAPTER 17

To raise a Genie to fight a Genie,
is a most dangerous thing to do.

—The Arabian Nights

On May 30, 1989, Gerry Bull wrote to his old
HARP colleague, Sannu Molder. Datelined
Brussels, the letter was headed *The SRC
Group of Companies*, and listed G.V. Bull as
president. For correspondence, three addresses were given: one was a post box in
Mansonville, Québec; the second, 63 Rue De
Stalle, Brussels; and the third, 52 Gloucester
Place, London. In the letter, Bull told Molder
that, "Our operations are spread over some
eight countries in Europe, the Middle East
and Asia. Travel is a pain. I live in aero-
planes. Secretaries keeping track of my
movements have figured out that over the
last 5 years at best I have not spent more
than 60 days in any one country in a year.
This makes me eligible for residence in the
sky."

The company, besides maintaining its
headquarters in Brussels, now had offices or
subsidiary firms in Austria, Greece,
Yugoslavia, Spain, Switzerland, England,
Liechtenstein, the Channel Islands, and

Canada. A number of old SRC-Q employees had been rehired, notably Bull's right-hand man at SRC-International, Louis Palacio. Consultancy and technology transfer were at the heart of the new businesses, as well as the development of new members of the GC-45 gun family.

Michael Bull says that the SRC Group was not a holding company in the formal sense. "First of all, you have to realize that there was no legal entity called the SRC Group. It really is exactly what it meant, a group of companies, nothing more. We started using that as early as '85, '84, when we started to realize we had more than one company. We needed to have one letterhead, or whatever you call it. It was not a legal entity. My father was not a board member of SRC corporation. Legally, he had no title. He was just an employee."

A flexible arrangement, to say the least, and one that provided no central knot from which the curious could easily trace the strands of their activities. The international aspect was further clouded by the repeated crossings of borders and jurisdictions. As Michael described it, "Since we were just one family [referring to the SRC Group], each company has a different type of infrastructure which, most of the time, was set up temporarily, and never would change anyway. They all differed one from another."

The result was a web of deals and interests that was truly global in scope. Outside of the Bull family members directly involved in SRC's operations, anyone who claims to fully understand what was going on is deluded. Large parts of the puzzle are still missing, and the relationships between various weapons systems, middlemen, clients, co-producers, technology sources, development programs and third-party cutouts, are so diffuse and open to interpretation that any attempt to view them in total simply flounders in a sea of data. The SRC Group was a series of expedients and *ad hoc* relationships that is best understood by starting at the end of the Bull story, and then working back along the major threads.

Gerry Bull's association with Iraq was to bring him both death and notoriety. It is, therefore, important to understand why, in spite of him calling the Iraqis "bastards," he was so attracted to the country. Equally, it is important to know why the feeling was reciprocated. The Persian Gulf war has created an impression among many in the West that modern Iraq is somehow a creation of Saddam Hussein's dictatorship. The notion that this Spartan little nation would have taken the same dark road to war, under any leader it might have produced, is not appreciated. But it should be, for the fuse to the explosion that became Iraq was lit a long time ago.

After enduring repeated national revolts throughout the '20s and into the 1940s, British colonialism in Iraq faded away in the winds of change that blew through the underdeveloped world in the early 1950s.

In a region then racked by poverty and disease, the emerging Iraqi nation was at the bottom of the statistical pit.

Female literacy was effectively zero. For men, it was under ten percent, and that mostly consisted of rote recitation from the Koran. One person in ten, out of a population guessed to be some seven million, was blind, as a result of eye diseases spread by polluted water. Except for a tiny elite, the average Iraqi could expect to live less than thirty-five years. Worse, oil, the country's one ace in the hole, was controlled by multi-national companies and, if the fledgling, coup-racked governments saw little of the wealth, the people got nothing.

Such was the country that, four decades later, would confront a coalition of the most powerful nations on earth. Remembering Michael Bull's quip that "hindsight is perfect sight," it is easy today to see that the warning signs were there from the beginning. Unlike many developing nations, Iraq never let sophisticated war machines rust out in storage depots, for lack of trained personnel to use and repair them. Nor did Iraq need to import thousands of foreign technicians to run its military, as nations such as Saudi Arabia must still do today. Long before Saddam Hussein came to power, successive Iraqi governments grasped a fact about modern war that still eludes most of their neighbors: while technologically sophisticated weaponry counts, the education of the people behind them counts more.

That Iraq conducted the world's most successful illiteracy-eradication program between 1978 and 1982 is virtually unknown in the West, outside of a small group of specialized educators. Because of the secular and progressive aspects of the dominant Ba'ath (Renaissance) political philosophy, women were educated at the same priority rating as men. Religious leaders who protested this were put in prison, until they agreed to issue statements supporting women's education. Few held out for more than a day or so. The end result was a population with the educational strength to forge an enormous military machine. As Saddam Hussein put it, "In Iraq today...the pen and the gun have one barrel."

A nation that was straining every effort to develop military and civilian technology was sure to appeal to Bull. Here, finally, was a country that was willing to take risks, to invest money in a unique way to orbit satellites. Project Babylon, the Super-Gun, the gigantic one-meter, smooth-bore cannon, whose parts would be discovered all over Europe, following Bull's death, is the stillborn proof of that desire.

Because it is so difficult to think of a gun as anything but a weapon, the idea that this big piece of pipe was some sort of ultra-long-range seige gun, for chemical, biological, nuclear or conventional high-explosive shells, fired against neighbors such as Israel or Iran, still has wide credence. Yet, try as they might, military analysts can find no utility in Babylon as a bombard. A system that weighs five thousand tons, and whose barrel cannot be trained or elevated once it is emplaced, does not make sense as a weapon, *unless one plans to orbit the warhead.*

Babylon, like the HARP launchers or, indeed, the American and Soviet space shuttles, must be seen as a delivery system, capable of delivering a wide variety of payloads into orbit, at very low cost. Hardened communications satellites, fuel, air or water supplies for manned space missions are possibilities, and so are weapons of mass destruction. It all depends on the user.

Contrary to popular belief, and press reports about Babylon being a "super-secret" undertaking, Bull made no effort to hide the project. He even gave interviews about Babylon in 1989, and a scale model of it was publicly shown at a May 1989, armaments exhibition in Baghdad.

Michael Bull says he warned his father against taking part in the Babylon project. He told him it was an unwise move politically, and that the views of outside powers toward Iraq possessing such a system might be severe. Since SRC was already heavily involved in Iraqi military projects, Michael's advice was sound but, according to Michael, Gerry ignored him and went his own way.

Considering that Iraq represented Bull's last chance of ever building his dream and proving the doubters and sceptics wrong, no one, least of all Michael, can be surprised that he went for it. Indeed, in retrospect, there is a doomed inevitability to it. While Bull's appointment with death did not occur in the Iraqi town of Samara, the road to his demise literally ran through it, north to Mosul, and the Sa'ad 16 Missile Development Complex. At sixty-two, Gerry was far from being young and, impatient as he was, he saw his own mortality, and heard the ticking of the clock. One line in his letter to Sannu Molder sums it up. "As I get older, everything takes longer, it seems, and weeks become like days."

Unfortunately for Bull, his timing was once again lousy. Nations, east and west, were waking up to the fact that the genie they had raised against the Iranian variety of Muslim fundamentalism was out of control. It was one thing for Iraq to acquire weapons to slaughter its neighbors, but it was another thing for the parties who had uncorked the bottle of Iraqi power to realize that it was seeking to develop weapons that could hit Moscow or Washington. Ignored for a decade, the concerns of defense and foreign-affairs analysts, about Third World ballistic missile proliferation, were at last given a serious hearing in world capitals. The question of what Iraq was doing, and who was helping them, was being asked by a score of intelligence and espionage services.

The query even made it's way back to Canada. In October of 1990, *The Wednesday Report*, a newsmagazine for the Canadian defense and aerospace community, obtained a large sheaf of documents relating to Bull's work for Canadian defense agencies, over a period of three decades. Buried in this material was an undated, once-secret report, prepared after his death for the government's Intelligence Advisory Committee of the Department of National Defence's Directorate of Scientific and Technical Intelligence. (DSTI) Entitled Bull: His Legend and Obsession, it is curiously inaccurate in some aspects, but it does contain this interesting speculation:

> SRC's ties with the Iraqis seems to have been strengthened in the late 80s. However, SRC's role, if any, in the extended range Scud is not known. The rapidity with which the Iraqis manufactured and fielded these weapons tends to indicate work of Bull's calibre. Although Bull was not a liquid propulsion expert, his entrepreneurial genius could have made it happen. No collateral exists, however, for such a theory. Nevertheless, his company was quite instrumental in Iraq's space program as open sources indicate that he even attended the El Abid space launch of 5 December 89.

About the same time, David Todd, a foreign-affairs journalist with Southam News Services, acquired the text of a letter, written two months before Gerald Bull's death by David Ryan, then the Director of External Affairs' Export Controls Division, to Michael Taschereau of the Canadian Security and Intelligence Service (CSIS). The Mr. Bull referred to is Michael Bull.

> As discussed obliquely on the telephone earlier today, it has been suggested to us that SRC of St. Lambert [Québec] may have been involved with Iraq government providing assistance for the development of a missile launched last month. This is purely rumour but Mr. Bull is known to have quote, excellent contacts with the Iraqi government and you will recognize the name of Bull and Space Research Corp in connection with illegal exports of weapons development with South Africa in the mid seventies. Obviously the involvement of a Canadian or a Canadian company with this missile project could be very embarrassing.
>
> A search of our records do not reveal any export permits being issued to SRC or Mr. Bull in the past several years. We would be grateful for any information you may be able to provide that would confirm or lay these rumours to rest. A copy of his business card is attached.

Michael Bull has confirmed reports that his father had aided the University of Mosul in setting up an aerophysics course, and had, indeed, given lectures there. Though Michael downplayed it, saying that he only gave "a few lectures here and there; they weren't class [sic] or anything this way. They were simply presentations, like dinner presentations...on his philosophy, and whatnot," it should be noted that this university is responsible for directing all scientific work at the infamous Sa'ad 16 missile development complex, outside of Mosul. Installations at the site include two wind tunnels and a long, underground firing range, of the type Bull pioneered over thirty years ago, at CARDE.

None of which ties Gerry Bull into helping Iraq develop improved SCUD missiles. Indeed, there is a good case to be made that he had nothing to do with it. The Iraqi development of SCUD derivatives has been well chronicled in the past decade and, since SCUD is a Soviet missile, it is not surprising that most of the assistance came from countries like the now-vanished state of East Germany. Time and circumstances predicate against Bull's involvement.

But, considering that Iraq was working on follow-on missiles to SCUD, and was seeking to establish its own aerospace community, especially the educational end of it, it is easy to see why suspicions were aroused. While agreeing that his father did attend the Iraqi test firing of a cluster-principle satellite launch vehicle, based on SCUD boosters, Michael points out that a lot of other people were also invited. The question is, how many of them were foreign scientists with a background in ballistic missile technologies?

Here, what Bull was actually doing becomes less important than the perception of what others thought he was involved in. Rogue and rebel that he might have been, his genius was acknowledged far and wide. His capability for brilliant improvisation and simple, inspired solutions to technical problems was so well known that, once the missile question arose, his services to Iraq could only arouse deep suspicions in nations both far and near.

Many theories have been evolved as to who killed Gerry Bull. Reports have surfaced, saying the Iraqis killed him because he was an Israeli spy, or that it was other Arab nations, jealous of Iraq. Michael Bull's original opinion was that it was the Israelis, and then he broached the idea that the C.I.A. did it, because his father was applying for a U.S. pardon of his arms-smuggling conviction. Charlie Murphy, a patriotic American, took exception to that view. "Have you ever considered that Canada might have done it?" he said.

We may yet see supermarket-tabloid stories on that line, but Murphy's point was that no one really knows who killed Gerry Bull. All one is left with is a list of suspects that gets less credible as the page grows longer.

Israel, and its dreaded Mossad intelligence service, does head the page, however. Considering that Israel has traditionally targeted technology development as the weak link in the acquisition of indigenous military power by its Arab neighbors, it is the logical candidate.

The Israeli bombing of the Osiris nuclear-reactor complex outside of Baghdad, on June 8, 1981, is the best-known case of such actions, but there have been many others. In the late 1950s and early '60s, the Egypt of Gamal Nasser launched an ambitious and, in the end, futile program to develop indigenous ballistic missiles. Many of the foreign scientists recruited were ex-Nazis, who had worked on Heinrich Himmler's SS missile experiments in World War II. When anonymous threats did not deter these men, a series of deadly letter-bomb explosions and mysterious accidents did. When the survivors were informed by unsigned letters, some found on their beds in tightly guarded Egyptian compounds, that they and their families were next, enough left to ensure the collapse of the missile project.

Even putting aside the missile-development issue, Bull's contribution to Iraqi armament capabilities was remarkable, considering the short duration it covered. Asked when their companies began doing business directly with Iraq, Michael Bull replied, "Our first contract, our first real visit, business-wise, to Iraq was in January 1988. That was sort of first investigations sort of things. The first contracts became effective in September, late September '88." As to the nature of the business, he said, "Well, unfortunately, I can't divulge everything. I'm still under an oath of secrecy. But essentially, you can say we worked on the 155 [and] the 210 self-propelled unit." (This latter device is an upscaled version of Bull's original HMSP/Rhino design, and will be discussed later, in the section dealing with Spain, in the next chapter.)

Other sources have suggested a more intimate relationship between SRC and Iraq, involving an extensive transfer of machine tools, design and technical assistance to the burgeoning Iraqi munitions industry, which began at least a year earlier than Michael Bull says. Michael was evasive on the role SRC played in these transactions, but he was willing to discuss Iraqi gun-manufacturing capabilities in some detail. Queried on whether Iraq could manufacture its own GC-45 type gun barrels, he said, "No. Not so far as I'm aware."

Then he went on to give this view of Iraq's capabilities. "You've got to distinguish between manufacturing stages. They did not have the capability to forge. They had the machinery to machine the barrels, that is, make the rifling inside. But, after saying that, let me put a word of caution in here. The fact that you have the machinery doesn't make you capable of doing it, either. We have seen them machine some very sensitive parts, in which the surface finishing was very important. They machined it, and then out of ten parts, they finally managed to do one properly. And you're almost clapping your hands saying 'Thank you very much,' and then he'd take the piece, put it on the floor, and kick it towards the store area, therefore ruining the surface finishing. There's no doubt the country was getting industrialized. But it has not achieved, in my opinion, a very high status."

Asked about Iraqi capabilities to produce their own artillery shells, Michael said, "We understand they had bought some machinery, and were setting up the line. But we never saw any shells produced by them. There is no question they were capable of making shells. They were making the 130 shell. It is our understanding that they had purchased the equipment to forge the 155." When queried about numerous European reports that this equipment had come from Germany, and that the companies involved are either under investigation or have been charged with violating German export laws, he said, "No, we don't know exactly where. I suspect South Africa."

One thing that South Africa did provide Iraq with was SOMCHEM expertise, in setting up the manufacture of advanced artillery propellants. Once again, much of the hardware for these plants is believed to be of German origin.

Perhaps the best-documented example of Bull's involvement with Iraq is the formation of SRC Composites. It is also an illustration of the complex and devious ways in which Iraq worked to acquire sophisticated technologies.

First, there must be a reason for the purchase that conceals or clouds the real reason for the acquisition. In his letter to Sannu Molder, Bull told him that "The SRC group is rather expanded. We have taken over the old Lear Fan carbon fibre aircraft company in Belfast." The purpose was to produce a single-engined, light aircraft of advanced design, to be made of super-strong, super-light composites. But, as Bull wrote, "The rights to the design rest with an American group of con artists. At first, we tried to deal with them, but abandoned the effort when typical American behavior emerged. Our studies indicate only a small market potential for the aircraft, and many design changes to be made before it is really up to its claimed potential."

This, indeed, may have happened, but it was the British government, particularly the Foreign Office, that stepped in to prevent the sale, that same year. On their recommendation, the Northern Ireland Industrial Development Board refused SRC Composites financial assistance to finalize the purchase. The main reason given was the sensitive nature of the carbon-carbon fibre technology. For the government had quickly discovered that SRC Composites was one hundred-percent owned by Canira Technologies. It, in turn, was fifty-percent owned by the Bulls, and the rest by the Technical Development Group, which was a hundred-percent subsidiary of the Al Arabi Trading Bank of Baghdad.

While the British, apparently prodded by the Americans, had moved swiftly in a matter involving high technology, they paid less attention to Bull's activities at the lower end of the technological scale. Their entire response to the "Super Gun" scandal shows it.

The week of November 12, 1990, all charges were dropped against the people and companies involved. Since U.K. customs sources had stated that the progress of their investigations was being "reported straight to 10 Downing Street," the end of the affair, from a legal point of view, was a great relief to the Conservative government. Their degree of support for Iraq in previous years was now to be swept under the carpet. But, in fairness, it must be pointed out that the cases were weak. Sheffield Forgemasters, which produced the barrel sections, and the engineering firm of Walter Sommers Ltd., which provided "aiming and elevation mechanisms," can thank their lucky stars they queried the British government on the propriety of the sales, and were told it was proper to proceed. Other charges against employees and associates of Bull's SRC group of companies seemed to have been dropped, in return for the SRC personnel cooperating with Western intelligence services to detail what Iraq actually got. The one positive result of this coverup has been the release of new information about the true nature of the transfers, which adds sense to previously known parts of the puzzle.

In August and September of 1988, when the contracts for Project Babylon were signed between Iraq and Bull, design work began immediately in Brussels. Among the SRC staff assigned to the project was Christopher Cowley, a fifty-two-year-old native of Liverpool, England, and an extremely competent metallurgist. According to Michael, his father went against his advice, and made Cowley head of a subsidiary Babylon project, variously known as Baby Babylon, Project 839, or System 350. "I told my dad I don't find Mr. Cowley all that dependable. He told me, 'No, no, no...you just don't know how to run people.' And he took him [with him to do the Babylon projects]. This happened some time in July or August of '88."

Michael Bull does not like Mr. Cowley, and perhaps with good reason. Asked if he was aware his ex-employee had turned state's evidence, he replied, "Yes, they granted him immunity." Michael said that Cowley was "a very, very convincing con artist. The trouble is he did know his stuff about metallurgy, but he cons and cons about the things he's done and his abilities." Michael then gave a confusing explanation of how he had previously wanted to fire the man, but wasn't able to do it. "I did not fire people who did not report to me. His superior boss would not fire him, because he was basically afraid to fire him." Referring to Alex Pappas, SRC's director of engineering, and Cowley's immediate superior, Michael said, "I finally put Pappas against the wall, and I told him, 'You've got a black sheep in your crowd, he's making everybody very upset. You either solve the situation or...We [Gerry and Michael] had agreed we would force Pappas to get rid of him."

That didn't happen. Bull went off with Cowley to work on the Babylon project and, a few months later, Michael said he received an urgent call from his father. "By Christmastime, early December, I was in Europe, and he [Gerry] called me. He said, 'Go to Geneva. I'm going through Geneva.' He was on a flight from Germany to Spain. He called me up and said, 'What do you think I should do with Chris Cowley? He's screwing everything up.' I told him, 'I hate to be the one to tell you, but I told you so.'"

Mr. Cowley would later tell the press that he resigned from SRC in April of 1989, because he was disillusioned with living in Brussels. Michael says he was fired. Whichever way it went, April was also the month that tests of a 350mm smooth-bore artillery tube system began in Northern Iraq. Michael Bull agrees with the original press reports that described System 350 as a test bed for the one-meter Babylon gun. He says the device was like the horizontal guns of the HARP project, without recoil or elevation devices, and that the failure was gas leaks from a jury-rigged sliding breech block. For the original test bed, that may be so, but as we shall shortly see, Mr. Cowley and British customs had a different story to tell, about the purposes of project 839.

Whoever was directing the effort, the Babylon projects were certainly on a developmental fast track. The previous February, SRC placed an order with its old nemesis, PRB, for 235 tons of a high-energy propellant, designated M-8-M and specified for System 1000, the one-meter gun. An order was also placed for some twenty-six tons of propellant for System 350. So urgently did the client want the material, that the first part of the shipment was flown out in a chartered Belgian air force C-130 transport, which departed Melsbroek air base in March. Its destination was Amman, Jordan.

Hedging its bets, SRC also placed an order with the French explosives company SNPE, for $5.5 million of similar propellants, which was scheduled for delivery in October 1990. Bull's death, and the discovery of Project Babylon, led the French government to cancel the sale.

In 1990, the British customs investigators, with Mr. Cowley's assistance, soon came to the realization there were two barrel systems involved in Project Babylon; the one-meter tube, and a 350mm one. According to Cowley, the ultimate form of Baby Babylon was to be a high-tech version of the ancient railway gun. It was for this system, not the one-meter tube, that the aiming and elevation system produced by Walter Somers were destined. With a 27.5-meter barrel, Baby Babylon would be capable of hurling a heavy shell several hundred kilometers.

In an article on November 7, 1990, the British newspaper, *The Independent*, claimed that American intelligence sources had informed them that Iraq received enough parts to assemble three of these devices, before the customs officials moved in, and that it planned to deploy seventy-five of them along its border with Iran. It is said that these cannons were to be mounted on railway tracks, enabling them to withdraw into hardened, underground shelters. The weight of the shell is given as fifty-two kilograms, and the maximum range as 750 kilometers! If these figures are correct, and some artillery specialists doubt them, it has been suggested that the projectile is simply a 155mm shell, saboted up to 350mm and equipped with a two-stage base-bleed unit.

Cowley has also revealed some details about the big Babylon program that make startling sense. In a conversation, aired February 13, 1991, by the CBC's French-language public-affairs program, *Le Point*, Cowley told interviewer Ann-Marie Dussault that the one-meter gun was to be laid up a mountainside in northern Iraq, in a location about seventy kilometers northwest of Mosul. Strongly denying any weaponry use for Babylon, Cowley said it would be pointed south, to fire research shells into a test zone in north-central Saudi Arabia. The distance between the given firing point and the target zone measures out at approximately 750 kilometers.

If deployed, the giant gun inevitably would have hurled its projectiles a lot farther than that. For, if one accepts Cowley's statements, Gerry Bull was, once more, thinking ahead. Plotting the geographic positions Cowley gives, on a globe of the world, reveals an interesting fact. Within the fan of angle possibilities, from the gun location to the almost unpopulated central Saudi desert, lies the optimum bearing for insertion into polar orbit.

On September 11, 1989, financially-troubled PRB was purchased by British-based Astra Holdings, for over forty million U.S. dollars. Astra, and its chief executive, Christopher Gumbley, had established a reputation for hard-nosed and aggressive expansion bids that bought cash-starved defense companies and turned them into profit-makers. The PRB takeover would not be one of their success stories. Soon after the purchase, Astra would commence a lawsuit against PRB, claiming fraud and misrepresentation of assets. Astra held up financing of the purchase agreement, and demanded a restructuring of PRB's operations. Stories appeared in the British business press, quoting Astra insiders as saying that many of the supposedly firm contracts in PRB's order books had turned out to be fakes, and the company itself had been stripped of "certain machinery and technical staff."

But Astra itself was undergoing problems. Allegations had surfaced that it had circumvented U.S. export-control regulations, and was involved in setting up an ammunition manufacturing plant for Iraq.

Gumbley himself would shortly be fired by Astra's board of directors, after he was arrested by U.K Ministry of Defence (MoD) police, on what is said to be an unrelated attempt to bribe a MoD official.

After Bull's death, Astra executive John Pike, who temporarily replaced Gumbley as Astra's CEO, would say they found another problem in the nature of some of the orders PRB did have. Specifically, they refer to the System 1000 and System 350 powder orders from SRC which, it is now said, were shipped out of Belgium under false papers. Pike says they informed the British government of these orders, and their doubts that Jordan was the actual customer. According to him, they were told it was OK to go ahead.

In a 1990 interview with David Todd of Southam News, Pike said that they first became aware of Bull's super-gun projects in November of 1989, when technical specifications for the super guns began arriving at PRB's offices, from SRC's Greek-based subsidiary, Advanced Technology International (ATI). Among the documents was a memorandum to Gerry Bull from Alex Pappas in Athens.

While the events Pike describes are factual, Astra's protestation of innocence in the affair is open to question. Rumors continue to circulate in the British defense community that Astra was involved in the shipment to Iran of a huge, American-built lathe, designed to turn large-diameter gun barrels and, according to some sources, its connection with Bull's activities may go back years.

But, as Michael Bull keeps reminding us, most of this is hindsight and the reporting of opinions and estimations. Back in 1989, the truth, to Gerry Bull, must have appeared quite different. His life's dream, the mighty orbital gun, was no longer sketches and engineering diagrams. Piece by piece, it was at last becoming a reality. In England, the barrel sections were leaving Sheffield on a regular basis. In Spain, the rollers to support the mighty tubes were being machined, and in Italy, the breech blocks had already been forged. Switzerland and Germany were providing hydraulic cylinders and other components. Powder charges were being produced in Belgium, and from Greece, a steady stream of purchase orders and technical data packages went out on a daily basis. And somewhere, a rocket-boosted shell was being designed, and the problems of guidance and telemetry return addressed. It must have seemed like the days of the HARP project had returned, and more, that vindication was at hand.

Other eyes saw it differently. In the shadowy fraternity of Western and allied intelligence agencies, a storm of questions was swirling around Bull's activities. Like any herd activity, the knowledge that inquiries were being made set other investigations in motion. The storm became a hurricane, with Bull seemingly oblivious to it all in the calmness of the fury's eye. It even reached the junior levels of Canadian army intelligence in Germany. As one enlisted man, stationed there in 1989, put it, "Everybody was talking about Gerry Bull...there was endless speculation as to what he was up to."

Why was Bull seeking information about liquid rocket propellants? Could he really supply Iraq with advanced guidance technologies for ballistic missiles? Just how much help was he giving the University of Mosul Aerophysics Department? The deadly potential of Bull's genius, as distinct from what he was or was not doing, began to play a larger role in the assessments. What would this man do next?

By the beginning of 1990, the question shifted again. It now became: how is this man to be stopped?

CHAPTER 18

In 1984, the Bull family, as distinct from Gerry Bull, purchased a house in Spain, on the Costa del Sol near Gibraltar. Some have described it as a mansion, but it is not quite that. A comfortable, four-bedroom villa, typical of many vacation homes in the area, it sits high in the coastal mountains, near the town of Mirbella. While the sea is three kilometers away, the gently curving Mediterranean beaches can be clearly seen from the villa's rear terrace. As Michael Bull puts it, "The view's all right."

This pleasant retreat often served as a meeting place for Gerry, Mimi and their now-scattered brood of children, in the years following its purchase. It was a place where any member of the family could show up at any time. Gerry would often use it for a few days of solitary rest, and a chance to think out some particularly challenging technical problem, in peace and quiet.

Of course, the climate and the view were not the only reasons for Gerry Bull's visits to Spain. It had been a way station in the 155mm-shell shipments to South Africa, and the one-time head of the old SRC-International, the Cuban-born Louis Palacio, had many friends and connections there, stretching back to the days of Barrios Hermanos and the South African transfers. According to Michael Bull, SRC opened an office in Madrid as early as 1984, and he says that it was one of their first expansions beyond Brussels.

The actual execution of their Spanish affairs would take the Bulls to the Basque provinces in the country's north. It was there that SRC's designs for improved versions of the GC-45, and more powerful conventional artillery pieces, were to be made real. In spite of a small, but violent, local separatist movement, the region, which had been one of the first areas of Spain to industrialize, was prospering, as the nation threw off the legacy of the Franco dictatorship. Like the rest of the country, the Basque region was rapidly developing a modern economic base, and there were many new and aggressive companies being formed, which were hungry for business.

Typical of the new, high-technology businesses sprouting in the area was Trebelan S.A., which was established in the Basque capital of Vitoria in 1983. An engineering consultancy firm, it specialized in military and civil projects in the fields of mechanics, electronics, robotics, technical data processing and production systems. In 1989, a company brochure stated that they had opened an "industrial division" in 1986, to manufacture "heavy artillery guns in calibers 105mm to 203mm self-propelled."

Besides Trebelan, Bull and SRC quickly established relationships with other members of the country's growing defense industry. One of these projects was a development of the GC-45, the FGH-155 long-range gun. Designed in SRC's expanded engineering offices in Brussels, the product was simplified and re-engineered, to eliminate over thirty percent of the parts required to produce the Austrian GHN-45.

Development of the FGH-155 was to have been carried out by SETSA, a joint venture between one of Spain's major ammunition manufacturers, Union Explosivos Rio Tinto SA, and the SRC group. One the executives of SETSA was Louis Palacio. Here, again, business conflicts arose between the Bulls and their new partners, and the co-production venture fell apart. Development was then carried out by SITECSA, a wholly-owned subsidiary of ERT, the conglomerate that owned Rio Tinto. SRC's role became that of a licenser, plus providing drawings and technical advice. In 1985, initial design studies for the gun were completed in Brussels, and a prototype was assembled at the Trubia plant of Santa Barbara, a long-established Spanish artillery-maker. The breech blocks used on the prototypes were produced by NORINCO of China. As of February 1991, the FGH-155 had not yet entered production, although there seems to be an order from the Spanish army for an unspecified number of these weapons.

SRC also entered into another agreement with a Spanish company in 1986. In conjunction with the ERT group, FORTEX SA, a Vitoria shell-forging and machining plant began setting up to produce a version of Bull's long-nose shell. By 1988, FORTEX was advertising it's new product in military magazines of Europe; *MILITARY TECHNOLOGY* being one example.

Another innovative SRC Spanish venture was developed in the late 1980s. The FGH-203 203mm field gun is a weapon that may lead to another Bull-conceived artillery revolution. By mounting the far bigger 203mm barrel on an FGH-155 carriage, a lightweight weapon, which greatly increases the reach and weight of shell of battlefield guns, is created. It has a range of up to fifty kilometers, with a shell almost three times the mass of a 155 round. Sodena, an industrial-development corporation based in Navarre, Spain, has provided financial assistance to this still-evolving project.

In early April 1989, the small airport at Vitoria was besieged by crowds of curious people, who came to see an unusual sight. Dwarfing the terminal building, the world's largest commercial aircraft squatted beside the runway. Ignoring a cold drizzle, dozens of photographers and camera crews from the local media photographed the huge craft. As they snapped away, hundreds of paid-ticket holders patiently waited to file through the cavernous cargo bay of the gigantic Antonov An-124 cargo jet. Most of the watchers assumed the plane was there on a good-will visit, but the Antinov was actually under commercial lease from the Soviet airline Aeroflot, and it was there to do a haulage job for Trebelan SA.

On the night of April 4, when the mighty cargo-lifter cleared the runway and turned east into the darkness, its destination was Baghdad. Lashed down in the cargo bay was a huge, 48-tonne vehicle. Sporting six 21 X 25 tires, the monster 210mm self-propelled gun had a two-section barrel, over 11 meters in length, which is believed to be of French origin. This monster mobile cannon could fire a 109.4-kilogram projectile to the incredible range of 57.3 kilometers.

Winging its way to Iraq was the old HMSP, in a new, Spanish-made incarnation. Unlike the South African G-6 Rhino, with its rigid frame, this new self-propelled gun had the articulated chassis of Bull's original design, and a massive, supercharged Mercedes diesel engine to propel it.

On April 28, the Al Fao, as the Iraqis named it, would be prominently displayed at the first Baghdad International Exhibition for Military Production. Spokesmen for Iraq's Military Production Authority (MPA) would tell defence journalists that development of the 210 system began in 1987. Trebelan SA of Spain provided the engineering support to build the first experimental chassis. The Al Fao also has a smaller brother, the Majnoon, which mounts a sectionally-extended, 52-caliber, 155mm barrel on the same chassis.

Some commentators have claimed that these weapons are already in Iraqi service, but Michael Bull says that is not so. "They never got beyond the prototype stage. We keep being asked by all these [government] agencies, 'What is the true situation? Do we have to fear these things in the Gulf war?' We say, 'Hell, no, the 210 never fired.'"

Spain, of course, made its contribution to the Babylon project. A. Paukner SA is a consultancy firm, registered in the Canary Islands. The company represents numerous German companies in Spain, such as Krauss Maffei, producer of the Leopard main battle tank. In February of 1988, the president of A. Paukner, Gerd Paul Paukner, the son of founder Anton Paukner, established a firm called Martec SA. One of the executives of this new company was Louis Palacio. In cooperation with Trebelan, Martec provided the export arrangements for the Al Fao cannon, and carried out liaison with the German and Spanish companies producing Babylon components.

After Bull's death, the Spanish government, prodded by a series of articles in the magazine *El Pais*, launched an investigation into the activities of SRC, but no charges were laid. The Bull family, which holds the rights for the various Spanish-produced cannon, are expected to continue the SRC ventures in that country, and to make it their base for future operations.

Many reports have said that Gerry Bull never returned to Canada, after his imprisonment. That is not true, though the visits were of short duration. Many years, he spent the Christmas season at Highwater, and he was known to regularly attend a New Year's ball in Montréal. These trips caused Bull another problem with the Canadian government, one that particularly infuriated him. They would not give him a new passport, because he took out American citizenship.

As Mimi Bull told it, "The story is that Gerry took his U.S. citizenship mostly because they needed him, and that was the only way he could get the clearance, so the citizenship was retroactive. He never thought he would lose his Canadian citizenship...[In the past] he kept working with the Canadian government on very classified matters. He reminded them many times that he had the U.S. passport also, and they said 'Don't worry about that, it's just a passport, you're still a Canadian.' [Later] his Canadian passport had lapsed for a year, and somebody told him that he had lost his Canadian citizenship and Gerry said, 'That's impossible. How can I lose my citizenship? I never left Canada, I was always a resident of Canada, I have no residence in the U.S.,' and they said, 'Well, try to get a passport, and you'll see.'

"So somebody knew that he had lost it; I don't know how they found out. It was a U.S. person, and when he did apply to renew his passport, he was told that he was no longer a Canadian citizen."

Asked if the Canadian government had officially refused him a passport, Mimi replied, "It was official, in the sense that he got back his birth certificate and his picture, and they said that the check will be mailed to you in a separate envelope. I never got the check back."

As for business activities in Canada, SRC maintained several offices in Québec after the mid-eighties. Potton Industries Technique, in the Highwater area, was among them, as were two SRC offices in Montréal. One was Construction SRC, a subsidiary of the Bulls' Swiss-based SRC Engineering. These firms are all small offices, with no staff other than secretarial help. When asked the purpose of the Geneva SRC Engineering, Michael Bull said, "It arose from the need to have one commercial body to sign all our contracts...it was a sort of clearing house. It functioned as a prime contractor for our various activities."

Just what the purpose of Construction SRC was is not known, and Michael was reluctant to discuss the matter. However, one can specu-late that it provided a convenient base point to oversee some of SRC's American dealings, as SRC made several purchases in the United States, during the latter part of the 1980s. Asked what business they did there for Iraq, Michael mentioned the acquisition of sophisticated computer-assisted design (CAD) work stations, for engineering use. According to him, "All these sales were entirely legal...with all the required documentation provided to...and approved by the U.S. govern-ment."

If the Canadian government was unwilling to have anything to do with Gerry Bull during the 1980s, the American one was not so reti-cent. According to Charlie Murphy, he and Bull made a joint proposal to a Pentagon organization called DARPA (the Defence Advanced Research Projects Agency), in 1985, to investigate the use of gun launchers for Star Wars anti-ballistic missile (ABM) systems. They were turned down, and Murphy used the refusal as another example of BIG SCIENCE thinking. As Murphy ruefully put it, "They said it was an interesting idea, but the technology was old, therefore it wasn't cov-ered by their mandate."

One interesting sidelight to Bull's dealings with the American gov-ernment is his filing for a pardon of his 1980 conviction. Bull began the legal paperwork in 1989, and the appeal would have been sent directly to President George Bush. The C.I.A.-assassination theory, which Michael Bull at one time considered possible, is based on the assump-tion that this legal process would open up a can of worms for the U.S. government, and so Bull was eliminated. While the appeal for a pardon was driven by Bull's conviction that he was innocent, there was cer-tainly a secondary reason. Persons convicted of a felony cannot, under U.S. law, be granted a security clearance.

However, Aberdeen and DARPA were not the only U.S. govern-ment agencies Bull talked to. From the days of his research on ICBM warheads, Bull had established connections with Sandia National Laboratories, a super-secret Livermore, California-based organization, involved in many nuclear weapon and missile-development programs. On more than one occasion in the mid-eighties, he sent them proposals for gun-based orbital launchers. Sandia did not pick up on those proposals, but it is interesting to note that, in 1989-90, they developed and successfully tested another one of Bull's ideas. It is a cheap, disposable, battlefield-surveillance device, consisting of a solid-state CCD TV camera/transmitter array in a 155mm artillery shell. Yet another link was to emerge in 1990. According to several aerophysicists who knew Bull, the horizontal, sixteen-inch gun in Barbados has been removed. The scientists say that Sandia has it.

Shortly after Bull's death, Saddam Hussein delivered a speech in which he threatened to "burn half of Israel with chemical fire." In the same address, he mentioned Gerry Bull. "A Canadian citizen with U.S. nationality comes to Iraq...He is a scientist...He might have benefited Iraq, I don't know. They say the Iraqi intelligence service is spread over Europe. But nobody spoke of the human rights of this Canadian citizen of U.S. nationality. After he came to Iraq, they killed him."

Stories about Bull's supposed meetings with Saddam Hussein are legion. Some reports in Canadian newspapers have said that Bull met Saddam as early as 1981. The Iraqi government supposedly sent a special plane to take him to Baghdad, for a clandestine meeting with the Iraqi leader in the back of a Baghdad tailor shop! Michael agrees that his father did visit Iraq in the year after his release from jail, but says it was nothing more than an exploratory business trip, and that he did not meet with Saddam. "My dad rode on a regularly scheduled Iraqi airliner...that's the special plane."

Other stories, carried in European newspapers, say Bull first met Saddam in early 1988. The claim is made that, during an audience at the presidential palace, he sat cross-legged on the floor with Saddam and delivered an extended monologue on his technological views. Michael Bull says these tales are "dramatic invention," and that his father never met the man. But one wonders about the latter comment. It is easy to visualize Gerry Bull sitting there, selling the moon and his dreams of orbital guns to an attentive, cold-faced man.

On March 31, 1990, while the press furor still raged over Gerry Bull's death, his family brought his body home to the country he had tried so hard to make a leader in technology. The scorned patriot, the boy who had dreamed his dreams in an apple orchard, and found pleasure in the sleek shapes of model aircraft, was returned at last to the soil from whence he came. That it was a country, which, in it's own blundering way, had driven him away, was no longer of any consequence.

Bull now rests in a cemetery in St Bruno, Québec. His passing was mourned by more people than the hundreds who attended his funeral. Thousands of men and women who worked with him, who knew him, or just understood the wide range of his dreams, grieved over his passing.

Others were not so charitable. Indeed, if there was a contest to determine which Canadian had the most influence on world affairs during this century, Gerry Bull would not win many votes from his fellow Canadians. People have called him a monster—a mass murderer—a merchant of death—a guy who got what he deserved. Derrick Blackburn, a member of the Canadian parliament and one-time defense critic for the New Democratic Party, struck a common chord when he said, "People who design weapons are morally deficient...a person like that is worse than a drug dealer."

Of course, now that he is safely dead, Bull has been attacked by many people outside of Canada, as well. Smooth-faced executives from Voest-Alpine have gone on television and implied that Bull's major problem was that he drank too much. Grossly fat, Middle-East arms dealers, men known for their double and triple crosses, have piously stated Gerry Bull was an unreliable business partner. Others, myself included, have used him as an example of some dangerous trends in world affairs.

But, in the end, it really doesn't matter. The man's life is over. Bull has been defined, stereotyped and locked away in the archives of a thousand media organizations. One small detail in the rush of events. Out at Highwater, the rust grows on the abandoned giant gun barrels, and the old launch control site is a vandalized ruin, the home of squirrels and spiders. Yet the memories of men who are no longer young have traced back the pathways and the lost hopes, and a light still comes on in their eyes as they remember Gerry Bull. "They were great times," one man said, with a sorrow beyond anger. "We believed we were about to do great things."

There is an anecdote about Napoleon that has some relevance to Gerry Bull. The French emperor was listening to a group of officers recommending a general to him. He was brilliant, they said, he looked after his soldiers as though they were his sons, he was courageous and spat in the face of death, etc., etc. Wearying of this paean of praise, Napoleon cut them off with a single question. "Yes," he demanded, "but is he lucky?"

Gerry Bull wasn't lucky. He was like the child in the school yard, who always ends up the leader of the group that gets beaten up. Yet, whatever one may think of his acts, he was larger than life. His mind belonged in a past when individual, mercurial thought, and disturbed brilliance, still had a place in Western affairs.

However, in another sense, Gerry Bull is still with us, still thumping the table and cursing those too stupid to see, too drained of heart to understand the thrill of challenge. For, like it or not, Bull was part of a great sea change in human affairs, and his activities go beyond the mere sale of cannon-making machinery, to the field of technical philosophy. In the light of the way so-called advanced nations now treat technology, Bull was a heretic. He was an individualist in a technical era that, for all its blathering about the importance of freedom to the inventive and developmental process, demands a collectivist mindset. He disagreed with the way the United States and Canada approached government-supported technological development. He could not abide the requests for proposals, the studies to see if there should be larger studies, and what is widely known as the "dreaded MILSPEC." (The American army's specification for chocolate chip cookies totals thirteen closely-typed pages!) He said it bred a cynicism that made the actual use of the specific technology almost irrelevant. In a bitter voice, he told me, "I found out America doesn't build guns to fight wars with, it builds guns to make money."

In his 1990 letter to Sannu Molder, Bull sounded a warning that was, in part, driven by his suppressed hatred of the governments that had rejected him, and in part by his honest view that North America had had it's day. "Europe is dynamic, changing rapidly technically. I believe it has surpassed North America. Having watched it recover from 1945, during the 1950s, until today is fascinating. The Americans do not seem to understand the box they have let their totally corrupt legal system paint them into. Within ten years they will understand, fully and sorrowfully."

It is easy to dismiss this statement as the petulant remarks of a scorned man, but Bull's belief went beyond simple anger, expressed in a letter to an old colleague. He had evolved a technological outlook that he called DCR (Dumb, Cheap, Reliable) technology. Bull saw this as a philosophical tool that Third World nations could use to bootstrap themselves into the twenty-first century. Not only in the military field, but in areas such as alternate energy sources, specifically solar, Bull predicted that underdeveloped countries would eventually leapfrog the West, because their drive to accomplish things is so much greater. "They have the need for excellence," he said. "They have the enemy knocking on the door." Not only did he believe that these countries would become "new centers of invention," but he saw them as actually using technologies that are already available, and doing it in innovative and cost-effective ways. He gave solar energy as an example of a technology that "doesn't require a penny of basic development; there's nothing new to find out about it, all that's required is a will to use it...America doesn't want it, [big] oil doesn't want it, so it doesn't get done."

Bull went on to say that DCR technologies are so potentially cost-effective that they are not very profitable, so governments and industries in the West shy away from them. He saw the evolution of technology along such paths making it an opponent of "so-called free-market societies...I believe that, in the end, technology is going to do more to destroy capitalism than all the revolutions in history. You think about that."

Asked if he promoted these views during visits and business meetings in underdeveloped nations, Bull replied, "You bet...every chance I get...I see a lot of enthusiasm, a lot of desire to get on with it...attitudes that are totally lacking in North America."

To return to more mundane levels, one must remember that most of the people Bull saw as having "a lot of desire to get on with it," were not purchasing solar cookers or irrigation pumps. It is important to realize that Bull is a prime example of a rapidly developing shift in global power. It is a occurrence of unfathomable consequences, which still continues today.

Developed nations, East and West, have been selling the products of military technology to the Third World for generations. In the 1980s, they began selling them the technology to produce their own weaponry on a massive scale. Rising literacy rates allowed country after country to achieve the "critical mass" of skills and talents required to make use of these technology transfers.

Western commentators often decry the example of nations, such as Brazil or Pakistan, spending huge amounts of money on developing military forces and the industrial bases to support them. Surely, it is said, they should be spending it on improving the lot of their impoverished masses. What these pundits fail to realize is that it is precisely the desire to improve the lot of their peoples that began driving Third World spending on military infrastructure, in the 1980s.

Control of shipping routes and resource-extraction areas are not subjects of great public interest, in developed nations. Westerners easily forget where much of the raw materials they consume comes from. Such matters are, more and more, talked about in areas as diverse as the Middle East and the Indian subcontinent. The idea that only the strong are listened to, or fetch a fair price for their goods, is driven by memories of five hundred years of colonial oppression.

Gerry Bull understood this view very well. "Hey," he said, "the Arabs are beginning to sense that their time is coming again...that may bring peace, it might be fifty years of war. I don't know, but it's coming."

Gerry Bull may be dead, but his ideas, like his guns, march on.